Queer Fish in God's Waiting Room

Queer Fish in God's Waiting Room

Lee Henshaw

Legend Press
Independent Book Publisher

Legend Press Ltd
13a Northwold Road, London, N16 7HL
info@legendpress.co.uk
www.legendpress.co.uk

Legend Press publishes contemporary, high-quality fiction
for the modern mainstream market. Our list is rich and varied
and aimed at providing readers with a different, thought-
provoking perspective. All of our titles are available to buy
directly (with special discounts and editons available) at our
website: www.legendpress.co.uk

British Library Catologuing in Publication Data available.

ISBN 978-0-9551032-85

Set in Times
Printed by J. H. Haynes and Co. Ltd., Sparkford.

Cover designed by Gudrun Jobst
www.yellowoftheegg.co.uk

Legend ▌Press
Independent Book Publisher

For Tim, who left us far too early.

I wrote this book to ask a girl to marry me.

It contains instructions on how to build a blackcurrant bath bong, and features a talking fanny…and she still said yes.

'Let every man take care how he talks, or how he writes of other men, and not set down at random, higgle-de-piggledy, whatever comes into his noodle.'
Sancho Panca

LIAM KERBY

I went to New York with my brother James and my great friend Ed Lover. It was winter and Brother James had just turned 21. Me and Ed Lover were a few years older.

The following year the three of us visited Mexico City, and it was just after that holiday that I met My Claire.

In Caracas were me and My Claire, Ed Lover and his Mexican girlfriend Ursula Paradise, and, without a girlfriend, Brother James.

BROTHER JAMES

Brother James is my hero. He slays dragons with his wit.

   He says things like, "Why wasn't Jesus born in Macclesfield? Because they couldn't find three wise men and a virgin."

ED LOVER

"I've got this theory about you and Claire," said Ed Lover. "Do you want to hear it?"

"Yeah, go on then."

"Really?"

"Yeah, definitely."

"Well, I look at you and Claire and I see two people who are really happy and I think, 'Why? Why the fuck is that?' And do you want to know what I think? And I've been thinking about this."

"I'd love to know, mate."

"OK – clap me in – it's because you're proud of each other. You can tell Claire is really proud of you and I know you're proud of her, and that's why you're both so happy. If you think about Jenny, she wasn't proud of me; she thought I was a dick. She didn't like it when I talked about Che Guevara. She wanted me to be somebody I wasn't. And Emma wasn't proud of me…she just admired me."

"I'm proud of you mate," I said.

"Yes, I know that," replied Ed Lover, "but I want somebody who is proud of me and wants to fuck me."

"Ah."

That's how it is with Ed Lover – every conversation is an education.

MY CLAIRE

My Claire was in bed reading. As I came to bed I turned off the big light, leaving the bedside lamp to dimly light her book, a popular tale about a child wizard.

"Can you read all right?" I asked.

"Yes," she replied softly.

"Not having any difficulties with the big words?"

"No darling," she replied, looking up at me and smiling lovingly.

My Claire supplies me with inspiration when I doubt that the human spirit can be carried forward.

'But what if it is not dirty but it is only that you are trying to use words that people would actually use? That they are the only words that can make the story come true and that you must use them? You have to use them.'
Ernest Hemingway

NEW YORK IS THE BASIS OF TRUTH

"I am a fucking legend at oral sex," declared Brother James, idly leafing through the pages of his pornographic magazine and chuckling away to himself on the seat next to mine.

"Write a story about snot," he started.

I put my middle finger in my earhole, wiggled it, and continued to stare at my journal.

"What it does, why it's there," he continued, gently poking at my finger with the straw from his Bloody Mary.

I smiled as I ran my pen over the words that I had recently written:

I wonder if we speak too much, me and these pages. What if I were to stop writing? What would be missing?

A pretty blonde airhostess glided past our seats, turning to smile at a grinning Brother James.

"Oh my goodness, that's tremendous," he said, casually attacking my finger again. "She would definitely get it."

I glanced at the girl, but I was more interested in the cake that Brother James had left on his tray, an unwrapped blueberry muffin.

"What's your favourite film, Liam?" he asked, tapping the straw on the tiny screen in front of him, which was showing film trailers.

"*Withnail & I*."

"Never heard of it. Mine is *Die Hard*."

"Which one?"

"I think they're all as good as each other."

"Are you eating that?" I asked him, reaching for his cake with an eager hand.

"Fuck off," he snapped, slapping my wrist. "I'm saving that."

He slowly and delicately separated the cake's plastic wrapping, grinning at me all the time. He pulled the cake out, held it to his face and sniffed it, closing his eyes, curling his nose and tilting his head back in appreciation of its goodness. With faked reluctance, he passed me half of it.

"Thank you brother," I said, smiling back at him then stuffing the cake into my mouth.

The airhostess returned, and Brother James ordered another Bloody Mary.

"And for you?" she asked me without enthusiasm. I pursed my lips with her question – probably beer and peanuts, I thought – but, rather than wait for my answer, she said, "Is the question too hard for you?"

I was dumbstruck. Why did she say that?

"Hey, listen love," started Brother James, "you're an airhostess and he is a writer. I doubt that you've got any questions that would be too hard for him."

She glared at Brother James. He gave her a wide smile and held it until she turned away.

"Daft bitch," he mumbled, returning to his porno. "Imagine," he said, "if you got a monthly statement, like the ones you get from the bank, that told you how many wanks you'd had that month and what you were thinking about when you had them."

"I'd say you'd be deep in the fucking red with that account brother."

"You're not wrong," he said, proudly.

*

17

We arrived in New York's Hell's Kitchen district to discover that our room in the Aladdin Hostel, on 47th Street, Room 607, was a simple one with four bunk beds in it, and that it was piping hot, a welcome contrast to the cold December air outside. We chose the bunk nearest the door. It was the night before we were due to meet Ed Lover.

"Let's go to the pub," said Brother James.

"Great idea."

We found a local Irish bar called Scruffy Duffy's where we drank Guinness and played some pool, excited to be in New York because New York looked like it was going to be much more interesting than Macclesfield. Both of us were nicely oiled by several pints of Guinness and, even though it was only a short distance to the Aladdin, we took a taxi back. As it pulled over on 47th the Syrian driver surprised us with his fee. "Ah, I forgot to put the meter on; it's free. Merry Christmas boys."

"Nice one," said Brother James, "thank you very much."

We returned to Room 607 to find all the other bunk beds now taken, rucksacks resting on them like German towels. On the bottom of the bunk nearest ours, a big fat lad was fast asleep and snoring.

Brother James frowned at the floor, which was littered with tinfoil. He crawled into his bunk looking for equanimity.

"Good night brother," he said. "I love you."

"Good night brother. I love you too."

At four in the morning two Kiwis and an Australian crashed into Room 607, turned the light on and started talking at a gratingly high pitch. This caused me to bring my hands to my eyes and softly rub them as the bright and uncomfortable light tried desperately to make an enemy of me. I lifted my head from the pillow and reached for the bottle of water I'd left by the bed. I continued to warm up my right eye, which slowly creaked open.

Everything was blurred. I'd rolled a big spliff before bed, a 'bedtime bomber' as Ed Lover likes to call them. I turned my head and through one red eye started to concentrate on these three lads. They saw me looking at them and stopped talking, so I pushed my left hand out and managed a crooked smile.

"Hiya," I said, sniffing.

They went quiet so I twisted my smile into a grin

and left my hand hanging until, shortly, one of them came to get it.

"All right," he said. "I'm Smashed-up Face, that's Corey and that's Mike the Cunt."

"Nice to meet you," I said. "Goodnight."

My right eye closed.

*

In the morning, me and Brother James had breakfast with Smashed-up Face, Corey, Mike the Cunt and the fat lad, Fat Mike, who was from Newport in Wales.

Fat Mike told us that on the flight to New York he had made the mistake of lighting up a cigarette. When their flight landed, a small army of policemen scooped up Fat Mike and his friends and intimidated them with what he described as "the usual pig show" which ended with the policemen threatening to send him and his friends home, but then letting them go. As the policemen shouted at Fat Mike, all he could think about was whether or not they would discover that his washbag contained 25 ecstasy tablets which he and his friends were looking forward to sharing on

New Year's Eve.

Fat Mike had decided to come on holiday to New York because New York, he said, "attracts the artistic and the powerful like nowhere else and side-by-side they make exquisite purple and red fountains for our varying tastes". I wasn't sure what he meant by that but it sounded good.

Fat Mike lived in London. "What do you think of it there?" I asked.

"Ah, well, Liam," he began, grinning at me, "the London roundabout travels at approximately 130 miles per hour, which is around 50 miles per hour quicker than the other fast British cities like Manchester, Edinburgh and Liverpool.

"So it's because of this that you must be careful when you go to London," he warned, "because if you end up in London and start demanding it goes slower by doing slower yourself you'll undoubtedly fall on your arse, and there's every chance you'll not get picked up but spat out."

I told Fat Mike that what he had said was interesting to me because when I once visited London I immediately fell on my arse just trying to negotiate the Tube. Fortunately, I was lucky enough to be picked up by Crazy Legs, my good friend who worked as a caretaker at a special needs school in London's East End. He was also a source of exquisite weed. Crazy Legs lived in an ant-infested squat in West London's shrine to concrete, Acton Town, which is where he introduced me to the concept of a blackcurrant bath bong.

To make a blackcurrant bath bong you put the following ingredients in a bath: one bottle of blackcurrant cordial, half a bath's worth of cold water and any ice you have to hand. Then you slice the bottom clean off a four-litre plastic water bottle. Next, make a tinfoil cave, perforate its base with needle pricks and place your cave into the bottle's neck. You then sink the bottle ever so slowly into the water to just below its neck and stuff the weed into the cave. It is very important that you do not wet the weed.

Then, put a flame just above the weed and slowly start to raise the bottle from the water, causing the dry plant to pull at the flame and burn smoke into the bottle.

Once the weed has burnt out, you cradle the bottle with both hands, get a friend to remove the tinfoil cave, and quickly put your lips around the bottle's mouth. Then…bosh…you shove the bottle into the water to shoot the strangely cold and blackcurrant-flavoured smoky brew into your lungs.

A bath bong, Fat Mike and I agreed, is a great and dangerous thing. Do it too often and only lunacy will beckon – but as an occasional way to kick-start a meaningful conversation when you are on your arse, nothing better. And this is why Crazy Legs always says, "Liam, I'm a healer, not a dealer."

After breakfast we all returned to Room 607. Me and Brother James went straight back to bed while Smashed-up Face, Corey and Mike the Cunt chatted and smoked their weed through portable glass bongs. Fat Mike had gone downtown with his friends, who were all staying in the room next to ours.

"Did you hear that fat bastard cutting trees in the night?" asked Mike the Cunt about Fat Mike's snoring. "Fucking fat cunt, did you hear it?" Mike the Cunt was talking to me but I didn't want to answer him because I thought he was a cunt for scowling at me over breakfast as I was writing in my journal and eating pancakes and, beside that,

23

I was busy writing about my conversation with Fat Mike.

"Liam!" he shouted at me.

I looked at him with a vacant expression, and sniffed.

"What?"

"Fat Mike's snoring."

"What about it?"

"Did you hear it?"

"Yes."

"Didn't it keep you awake?"

"I preferred it to your whining accent," I replied.

"Fuck off...and what the fuck are you writing about?"

"How much I like you."

"Are you writing about yourself?"

"Among other things, yes."

"And do you write about your brother too?"

"Yes."

"And do you want people to read what you write?"

"Yes, I do."

"And take it seriously?"

"Yes. I want it to be, like Shelley said, 'the trumpet of a prophecy'."

"You pretentious twat…it'll never happen."

"Why?"

"Well, the answer to that is simple enough."

"Let's hear it then," asked Brother James.

"Well, James, the reason that I cannot believe Liam is a good writer is that he is so clearly a fool, and a fool should never write, or, at least, should never write well because, if he does, how on earth is anybody able to believe in his foolishness?"

"I think you are a great writer, Liam," said Brother James.

"Thank you brother," I replied.

"We'll see," said Mike the Cunt, standing up to leave the room for a piss, "we'll see."

He gave me a wink and a sly smile on the way out.

What a cunt.

It's amazing, when you think about it, how quickly you can get to know a stranger when you share a room in a hostel with them.

*

That morning, me and Brother James took a taxi to JFK airport. We found Ed Lover sitting outside

Arrivals reading a book.

"Lover," I shouted.

Ed Lover looked up from his Che Guevara biography.

"Nice," he mouthed, slowly and extravagantly, smiling as he got up and walked towards us.

*

Back at the Aladdin Hostel there was a note waiting for me at reception. It was attached to the notice board with double-sided sticky tape. I read it quickly. "Oh fuck," I said, pulling the note from the board, "Mrs Buckle is here."

I put my head in my hands.

I had met Mrs Buckle about a month earlier, spending no more than half-an-hour with her after meeting her outside a hostel on the Hawaiian island of Maui, while waiting for my new friend, Deadhead Garth, to pack his rucksack. When she kindly offered the pair of us a lift to the local airport, which was a good hour's walk from the hostel, we readily accepted.

Not the most experienced of travellers, I had given Mrs Buckle the phone number of the

Cambridge flat I was sharing with Ed Lover, simply because she had asked for it. I had also told her I would be in New York for the week around Christmas and New Year. She had then rung the flat, and Ed Lover, thinking she was a friend of mine, had told her when we would be arriving in New York and where we would be staying.

'Dear Liam', said the note, 'Remember me it's Mrs Buckle how are you I am staying here too will find you soon love Mrs Buckle.'

"Oh fucking hell," I said through my hands, "What the fuck is -"

"Hello Liam," said Mrs Buckle, who was standing next to a grinning Ed Lover.

Slowly, I took my hands from my head, leaving the note stuck to my forehead, and there she was, the enormous 35-year-old gothic Mrs Buckle, smiling right at me. "Ah, Mrs Buckle," I said, "what a nice surprise."

*

"You would definitely let Mrs Buckle sit on your face and pedal your ears, wouldn't you Ed?" said Brother James.

"Fucking hell, she hit a few branches on the way down, didn't she?" replied Ed Lover.

"Hey?"

"From the ugly tree. Me, I swung down it and landed on a bed of feathers. Mrs Buckle, picture it, she hit her nose on one branch, smacked her teeth on another and landed on her chin…what a beast!"

"Ed, you are an idiot looking for a village. Are you going to fuck her? Are you going to fuck Mrs Buckle?" asked Brother James of Ed Lover, who ignored him.

"Why didn't you just give her the wrong phone number, you fucking idiot?" Ed Lover asked me, just as Mrs Buckle let herself into Room 607, uninvited.

"Bollocks," shout-burped Brother James.

A shout-burp is an offensive thing invented by Brother James. To do a shout-burp you gulp lots of air into your lungs, think of something to shout and let it out at the same time as the air. It's really disgusting.

*

Mrs Buckle was a mother who looked like a

grandmother, with a face between unattractive and miserable. A clerk from Chicago with a seventeen-year-old daughter, she had very dark wiry hair, a low forehead, dull and unfriendly eyes and a brittle thin-lipped American mouth that, on an animal, would have been the mouth of a ferret. She must have weighed about 18 stone. Her chin was sunk and she had bad ears and a flat, almost a boxer's, pocked nose. This should not have added up to an intriguing face, but her voice, the way it demanded you find wonder in her, this pulled you in. The voice worried you until you knew it, and then it worried you even more.

Mrs Buckle had come to New York to spend New Year with three people she didn't know, and we were all at least ten years younger than her. For me, talking to her was becoming increasingly difficult because the more time I spent with her the more I discovered about her fetishes – she liked being "fucked in doorways", for example. What do you say to that?

I was getting the feeling she was here to see me. By the third day I had a few more notes from her and I wasn't looking to start a collection.

Room 607, late afternoon: discarded and manhandled beer cans looking curiously at their surroundings with their reshaped metal faces, elaborate bongs containing rank brown water flanked by useless tinfoil scraps, and my wild fucking dreams getting all the wilder.

In *Hamlet*, Shakespeare writes, 'O God, I could be bounded in a nutshell and count myself a king of infinite space, were it not that I have bad dreams.'

In my dream that afternoon, I had a smoke on the steps of a hospital before visiting my bridge-operating uncle, a recluse. On the way a short and unforgiving Italian doctor blocked my view so I tapped his shoulder and when he gave me a dirty look I took it with my camera. I drifted under busy bridges, by a little red lighthouse, and all the time I thought about home. When I got there – to the bridge – I found my uncle to be out and, according to my aunt, off his head. My dad, in this dream, was in the corner quitting smoking. My mum was in the kitchen refusing to cook properly. I believed everything at once and it made my head hurt. My brother wasn't there and I needed him there to make sense of it all, so I panicked and then woke up with a start to find that, of course, Brother James was there. In fact, he was above me, snoring.

*

All the eating, drinking and smoking weed was causing me great mental and physical discomfort, and I didn't know where it came from or why I inflicted it upon myself, and it was this, I thought, that must have been responsible for the awful and confusing dreams.

I looked at that morning's writing and judged it poor; it seemed sickly too:

Yesterday we saw the five boroughs of New York from a Circle Line boat (which leaves from 42nd and 12th), ate food in Little Brazil (on 46th, between 6th and 5th) and then Ollie's (on 44th between 8th and Broadway).

Saw a funny thing too in a jewellery shop, funny peculiar, a real-life pantomime.

A big black man wants to look at the gold

watches displayed in a locked cabinet and the tiny Asian shopkeeper makes it clear he doesn't want to unlock the cabinet by showing the man his back.

"Hey Bruce, what's wrong with you? I want to look at the gold...are we talking the same language?"

Bruce (Bruce Lee?) casually turns to face the man, reaches ever so slowly, without any show of nervousness, into his pocket to pull out the key to the cabinet, all the time acting as if he is about to let him see the gold. But he doesn't. Instead, he dramatically kicks at what must be a very small panic button under the counter because after a few of those kicks the shop door finally makes its unmistakable locking sound. "I am locked," says the door. "You are stuck in here; this is just like prison."

Bruce then closes his double-act with the door by lifting the handset for the phone and threatening to dial 911. "I dial 911; I dial 911," he says hurriedly.

"Phone the police then man – just let me out – fuck you!" bellows the man, grabbing a mirror from on top of the counter and aiming a pretend throw at Bruce. A pretend throw is one of those throws where you make all the necessary

movements to complete a throw but you don't actually let go of the object. Bruce flinches just a little before booting the panic button again. Click. "OK," says the door, "we will let you go this time but don't you come back and try fucking with us again...OK?"

The man shows his teeth to Bruce, calmly puts the mirror back where he found it, and twats the frame of the door with his fist on the way out.

"Didn't feel a thing," boasts the door.

Buzzing from being the only audience for that dramatic and ridiculous show, the three of us skipped to Central Park to meet up with Heinous Name Dropper, a friend of a friend who would make floorboards creak with the weight of his A-list celebrity friends.

Brother James had woken up and he was telling the room about how, the night before, a woman had approached Ed Lover on the street saying to him, "Let me suck your cock man; let me suck your cock for you". Ed Lover had told me about this after it had happened. He had described the woman as a "drugs prostitute".

Brother James said to Ed Lover, "Shit like

that never happens to me man; she was well into you."

*

Room 607, me and Heinous Name Dropper mid-conversation: "This failure to make contact with reality is, however, characteristic of almost all of America's art," said Heinous Name Dropper. "Any connection between American art and American nature is purely coincidental, but this is only because the nation as a whole has no contact with reality. That is only one of the reasons why I have always been forced to exist on the fringes of its society, consigned to the limbo reserved for those who do know reality when they see it."

"OK," I replied hesitantly, confused by what I had just heard because my mind was addled, intoxicated, seriously bent by the skunk weed I'd just smoked and, as much as I had tried to concentrate on what Heinous Name Dropper was saying, I had also drifted, leaving me unsure of what to say next. I was sure an important matter had just been discussed and although I had been listening I had also, as often happens, completely forgotten to concentrate and missed the point entirely, which was why I could think of nothing better to say than, "fancy a slice of pizza?"

"Of course, yes, of course, but, you must see, Liam, that what I am trying to tell you, is that I have been well and truly fucked by the fickle finger of fate."

"OK, but you are hungry?"

"Hank Marvin, mate."

"Great, let's go."

*

Twice, Brother James was mistaken for a woman in New York.

In the foyer of the Aladdin Hostel, the receptionists were looking for the person who had booked a taxi to the airport. "Lady," one of them shouted at Brother James, "did you book this…?"

Brother James turned to look at the man and scowled.

At the time I was on the phone talking to my good friend in Washington, Adam Bigone, casually following the trail of the receptionist's query to Brother James's disgusted face, then laughing my ass off while trying to tell Adam Bigone what had just happened.

And in Scruffy Duffy's, the night we had arrived in New York, some random woman told Brother James, "Don't be frightened of who you are!" She refused to believe he wasn't a lady.

"I should have got my fucking dick out and fucking pissed on her, the big daft bitch," he said in the taxi on the way back, clearly annoyed. Brother James had a blond flop styled to resemble the one David Beckham had at that time.

Instead, he looked like a ladyboy.

Well, he didn't. Not really.

But that didn't stop me and Ed Lover telling him he did.

We were amused because Brother James is a Macclesfield lad and Macc Lads pride themselves on looking and acting like Alpha males. They cannot entertain the idea that they look even remotely effeminate, even when they do.

*

"She does have one thing going for her," started

Brother James.

"Who, Danny?" I asked.

"Yeah," he said, grinning and nodding his head in approval.

"What's that then?"

"She sucks like a Dyson."

"Jesus Christ James, you've got a filthy mouth."

"And she was a squirter."

"A what?"

"A squirter. Have you never been with a woman that squirts?"

"Clearly not."

"Oh, it's great. When she comes, a load of stuff shoots out of her…" he paused, not knowing what word to use with me, "fadge." He started laughing his infectious laugh and despite myself I smiled.

"I'm not sure what it is," he continued, "it could just be wee." We were in Room 607 resting on our bunk bed. Brother James was eating the last of the meringues from a box of meringue nests he'd bought to snack on. He threw the empty pack at me.

"Look at what it says now."

He'd used a pen to scrub out the e's and the r

from meringue so that it read 'minge nests'. I threw it back at him.

*

Mrs Buckle barged into Room 607 the afternoon we were due to leave for Washington, telling us it was impossible for her to fly back to Chicago because of the heavy snow and, if we didn't mind, she would come and join us on our trip to Washington.

As Brother James and I giggled and looked at our shoes, Ed Lover made it clear that we didn't want her in Washington by suggesting she get the bus back to Chicago.

Lost for words, and clearly annoyed at being rejected by us, Mrs Buckle snorted and left the room.

"Ed Lover, that was well tight," said Brother James.

"Fuck you James, and fuck you too Liam; you were both too fucking frightened to say anything to her – you're a pair of fucking pussies."

*

On the train to Washington, Brother James was reading a film script written by Heinous Name Dropper – "This is shit," he commented – Ed Lover was playing Tetris and I was listening to a Spikey Tee album and writing.

Chocolate-chip cookies and crisps. Chocolate-fucking-chip cookies and crisps. Why can I not stop eating chocolate-chip cookies and crisps?

"Oh, I've fucked it…bollocks," said Ed Lover, throwing the Tetris at me.

Sitting opposite me was an untidy Latin American woman who was headbanging without the help of music. Watching her head quickly twist this way and that, her eyelids dramatically closing in order to appreciate something, then snapping open to wildly hunt the air around us for something else, I was reminded of a party I went to when I was ten-years-old.

A popular girl at school called Pub Landlord's Daughter threw the party, and it was there, along with several other ten-year-olds, that I discovered the joy of headbanging to heavy metal music. On the Monday morning, the lot of us turned up at school wearing oversized foam collars to protect our injured necks, causing the headmaster,

Mr Snot, a dreadful alcoholic, to give an assembly about the ills of headbanging. This assembly would alienate me almost as much as the one I would attend six years later when our Catholic headmaster lectured our school about the fact – "fact", he said – that the film *The Life of Brian* was evil. Knob-end.

*

Washington's New Carrollton station was covered with thick snow when we arrived. We were met at the station by Adam Bigone and his fiancée Shagging Pickpocket, daughter of Mr and Mrs Pickpocket, whose home we were staying at. Mr and Mrs Pickpocket were Republican lawyers who had an enormous house on a hill.

*

"How are you, Adam?" I asked, brushing my teeth as my old friend stood next to me, having a piss in one of the many upstairs bathrooms in the Pickpockets' house.

"I'm good mate; what about you?" replied

Adam Bigone.

"You know, not so bad," I said. "I like this bathroom."

The bathroom, like the rest of the first floor, had not been redecorated since the early 1970s. The paisley patterned wallpaper was a garish red, the ceiling was mirrored and a long thick red rope with a frayed end was used to turn the light on and off.

"Anything you'd like to do?" asked Adam Bigone.

"Yeah, kick your head in."

"Anything else?" smiled Adam Bigone.

"Well, I would definitely like to go to the *Star Wars* exhibition at the Smithsonian; that would be a treat. Capitol Hill would be good. The White House. And the Vietnam and Korean War Memorials."

"No problem, I'll get the car out now," said Adam Bigone. "And make sure you wrap up mate; like you said, it is freezing out there."

*

As Adam Bigone drove me, Ed Lover and

Brother James to the Smithsonian, Mr and Mrs Pickpockets' dogs, a pair of Pugs, were investigating Brother James's suitcase. It lay on his bed, open and defenceless. At first, the Pugs were happy to sniff his clothes and pull them out playfully: his big Tommy Hilfiger coat, then a Ralph Lauren shirt. Gently they wrestled for possession of each item as it left the case, covering his clothes in their saliva. Then their mood changed from playful to vicious when they came across a plastic bag stuffed with Brother James's dirty underwear.

As one Pug pulled it out of the suitcase, the other tried to take it from him, which split it. They trapped his favourite Calvin Kleins under their paws and viciously pulled at them with their teeth. Once they'd massacred his underwear, the Pugs turned their attention back to the suitcase, which was where Brother James also kept his porn mags. As if they knew what they had discovered could cause him maximum embarrassment, one of them scooped up a copy of *Lusty Lesbos,* the other grabbed an edition of *Asian Babes*, and together they took the magazines into the hallway and tore them into tiny pieces, littering Mr and Mrs

Pickpockets' first floor with disgusting debris. Fortunately for Brother James, Mr and Mrs Pickpocket, both committed Christians, had not seen the first floor of their home for the last seven years, their age and weight keeping them to the ground floor only.

*

On the train back to New York, I proudly proclaimed that by pissing on the White House lawn I had committed a federal offence. Brother James and Ed Lover rightfully ignored me for being dull.

That night we crawled through Greenwich Village and Lower East Side, visiting the White Horse Tavern, Bar 101 and Max Fish, where I was excited to see a sticker on a pool table for a great but sadly obscure Manchester band called *The Dust Junkys*.

As we played pool, Ed Lover was snuggled in the corner playing tonsil wars with Israeli Pie, a beautiful and buxom 20-year-old girl who had introduced herself to Ed Lover within minutes of us entering the bar.

Between those long kisses, she whispered to him, "I can't sleep with you tonight – if I do that I'll feel like a whore. I don't go out looking for men to pick up but you are beautiful. You could go over there, there to where those women are, and any one of them would fuck you. If you see me tomorrow, I'll do all the things I want to do to you – I want to play with you; I want to fuck you; you are so lovely."

We all went back to Max Fish the following night because Ed Lover was keen to experience Jester's toes with Israeli Pie.

"What the fuck are 'Jester's toes'?" asked Brother James.

"Think about it James," Ed Lover replied. "It's the shape your toes go just before you come. They curl like Jester's toes…or at least mine do."

Israeli Pie never showed. Ed Lover was gutted.

*

My camera no longer works. I was sat on a McDonald's toilet when my bag slid away from me. I jumped up, yanked open the door, rushed forward, hit my head on the cubicle frame, and bounced backwards to see the bag thief, Brother James, pissing himself laughing as my camera shot out of my pocket and landed in the toilet bowl.

On this good and funny day we also had a legendary snowball fight on the 9th floor roof-garden of the Aladdin Hostel. Up there, I found Brother James and Richard of Leeds (an architect that we had befriended in Max Fish) picking off pedestrians with snowballs. I snuck up on them and, from a respectable distance, landed a corker on the back of Brother James's head. After a brief battle with the two of them, they returned to the indiscriminate pelting of passers-by.

This ended with the concierge from the hotel opposite looking to protect his guests by screaming, "You hit my hotel man; I'm gonna come up there and kick your asses." Obviously we launched a tirade of snowballs at him and then legged it when he hurtled across the road to get us. In Room 607 now, Brother James is back from the lobby. He'd rushed back here and immediately changed his clothes so that he could go down to reception and witness the concierge's rage.

"What a fucking dickpump," said Brother

James, shout-burping the word 'dickpump' to emphasise this. The concierge had entered the lobby to hurl obscenities at the receptionist, most of them concerned with the calibre of guest that the Aladdin Hostel attracts.

*

I'm trying to sleep. Can't. Six big slices of pizza and an oversized bruschetta are keeping me awake. I am thinking about writing – can I knock on silence and make a sound?

*

I was enjoying the story of King Minos. When King Minos was away at war, his queen, Pasiphae, was fucking a bull. The bull was a sign from the god Poseidon that King Minos's leadership of the Cretan empire was just and proper. To seduce the bull, Pasiphae had the artist-craftsman Daedalus build her a hollow wooden cow; she got in it, the bull was deceived and, following a few rigorous sessions, Pasiphae was pregnant. Daedulus was then commissioned by a sympathetic King Minos to build a tremendous labyrinthine enclosure, and that's where her child, the Minotaur, grew up.

*

On the morning of our last day in New York, Ed Lover asked Brother James, "What are duds? How the fuck do you 'put a decent pair of duds on'?"

Brother James was wandering around Room 607 in just his towel, hunting for a clean and stylish pair of underpants.

That afternoon, at the Museum of Modern Art, we met up with Heinous Name Dropper and his wife Yuko (disproving our theory that he had invented her). We saw the Jackson Pollock painting Pasiphae, a dedication to the bull-seducer – "This is shit," opined Brother James – and later we stood in the Imagine circle, a tribute to John Lennon, who was shot outside the hotel nearby. At JFK we boarded a plane home, the last journey the three of us would make together until we went to Mexico the following November.

'Anyone can buy seven-cent-apiece eggs for seven-cents-apiece.'
Milo Minderbinder

QUEER FISH IN GOD'S WAITING ROOM

It was late at night in London's Manor House when Brother James arrived, his gentle tap, tap, tap on my window inviting me to open the curtains to find his cheek and forehead pressed against the glass, one sparkling green eye looking for an overdue hug. Grinning, I rushed into the hallway and opened the front door, and in he strutted to announce he'd had "a fucking 'mare getting here". He'd managed to miss his bus stop and got off in Tottenham, where the sight of so many gangs of lads looking at him inquisitively – Tottenham doesn't get many backpackers – had him diving into the back of a passing black cab.

"I was shitting it," he admitted, stumbling into the lounge, dropping his rucksack, collapsing on my sofa and then taking off his shoes to reveal a bundle of holiday money stuffed inside each sock.

He wanted food and beer so I took him to Green Lanes, a colourful main road with countless kebab shops and members-only gambling dens for the Greek, Turkish and Kurd communities.

"Brother James, you have to be Turkish to get in that one; there's no way they'll -" I said as he opened the door to one of the dens, to a room that's no longer mysterious to me. Once inside he simply strolled between the two scruffy pool tables, nodded at the group of dark-skinned moustachioed card-players and said to the Turk at the makeshift bar, "All right pal, two beers please."

Twelve hours later, following much drinking and very little sleep, I was scoring weed from Crazy Legs in Acton Town while Brother James was back at mine entertaining Ed Lover, who had come to us from Cambridge.

Brother James and Ed Lover had bought fireworks, and that night they put on a show, during which Brother James yelled, "Ed, don't be such a fucking puff," well within earshot of our gay neighbours. Ed Lover was warning Brother James not to return to a lit firework.

The next morning we flew to Miami.

*

"A lovely location boys," said Ed Lover, looking towards Miami's Ocean Drive from our hotel room, which had one double bed and one single bed, art-deco soft furnishings and complimentary plastic cups for coffee.

"Are you writing your journal Liam?" asked Ed Lover.

"I am," I replied.

"Well, don't fucking put me in it."

"I have to brother."

"Well, don't fucking misrepresent me then. Say that last night we went to a semi-titty bar, well, more of an arse bar, and afterwards I tried to stop you buying those twelve finger-rolls and all that cheese."

We'd arrived at our hotel one hot morning ago delighted to be close to the home of fashion designer Versace, who hadn't lived there since somebody shot him on his front steps not that long before.

"Did you know Miami is the Bentley capital of the world?" asked Brother James, putting pieces of cheese between the beautiful, sugary finger-rolls as he rested on the bed, the air-conditioning keeping his back cool.

"You want to watch the film *Scarface*," said Ed Lover, ignoring Brother James and punctuating his sentence with a loud fart. "It'll tell you all about the Cuban prisoners who came here."

Ed Lover, by the way, takes great pleasure from farting in public and blaming it on other people, always me if I'm with him. In the queue for customs at Miami airport, he let off a 'silent-but-violent' and managed to convince the passengers immediately in front and behind us that I was responsible for the odious smell. To do this he fell out of the queue with a few exaggerated steps, pulled a pained expression, waved one hand in front of his nose and pointed at me with the other. A Geordie behind me laughed heartily as Ed Lover then swore blind he'd seen my coat-tails flap from the wind.

"What do you think Mr Kerby?" asked Ed Lover, who was wearing nothing but an oversized pair of elasticated, blue cotton shorts with a red zigzag, his body looking painfully white and skinny. He was asking me for advice about what he should wear to the beach, but I was too dazzled by the sun bouncing off his whiteness to reply immediately. "Fuck it mate, I'm wearing my tracky bottoms instead," he said, impatient for an answer.

The bread had gone by then and the crisp and cheese piles were getting smaller and smaller.

"It's good to see it's not only in England we have a ridiculous fascination with boy bands who don't think they're boy bands," said Ed Lover, flicking between the TV's channels as he changed.

"Tell me something Ed," I asked, interested in his opinion on a newspaper article I was reading. "How do you feel about drug-testing at work?"

He thought for a minute before a big magnetic grin spread across his face.

"Well, I wouldn't sack somebody for it, but I would consider taking them aside and having a quiet chat if they tested negative."

*

I had started keeping a food diary. I thought that having a record of all the things I was eating would shame me into eating less.

Saturday

- *11.20am: Fresh orange juice, bacon and eggs, toast, coffee and a chocolate muffin. 3 cigs.*
- *2.40pm: Burger, chips, fries, chocolate milkshake, and an apple. 2 cigs.*
- *4.00pm: Chocolate bar and a can of coke. 1 cig.*
- *7.30pm: Steak and chips, ice-cream and a yoghurt. 2 cigs.*
- *8.30pm onwards: 7 bottles of beer and 4 rum and cokes. 10 cigs.*

Sunday

- *11.00am: Can of coke, chocolate bar and some muesli.*
- *4.00pm: Ribs with 6 beers. 4 cigs.*
- *8.00pm: Pizza with 2 beers. 3 cigs.*
- *11.00pm: 2 beers and 1 packet of cookies.*

*

"And another reason why I don't like smoking that shit is that it makes your throat feel all dry and horrible," said Brother James.

"Jesus was a smoker James," said Ed Lover.

"Shut-up, you dick," replied Brother James.

"He causeth the grass to grow for the cattle, and

herb for the service of man…that is written in the bible," said Ed Lover. "It is the oldest natural herb on earth Brother James, and Jesus and all his followers were – and this is a documented fact – rubbing cannabis oil into each other temples and tripping their nuts off. So, if it's good enough for Jesus, it's good enough for me…and if you disagree with people smoking it, that makes you the anti-Christ."

"That is an absolutely fucking ridiculous point-of-view," responded Brother James.

"Do you still have the 4.20 rule at work Ed?" I asked Ed Lover.

"Of course," he replied.

"What's the 4.20 rule?" asked Brother James.

"Every day at 4.20 somebody in the office has to skin-up," said Ed Lover, matter-of-factly, as if this were commonplace.

"Why?" asked Brother James.

"Because I'm the boss and it's my favourite management tool," said Ed Lover. "I really think more companies should do it. It's a great way to alleviate stress in the workplace. I learnt it off some Deadheads I met in California who were running a very successful ice-cream business."

"What's a Deadhead?" asked Brother James.

"They're fans of a dreadful guitar band called *The Grateful Dead*," replied Ed Lover. "Lovely people. They're very chilled and they love a smoke, and when you ask them what time it is, they will always say, regardless of what time it actually is, 'it's 4.20 man,' then roll a spliff."

"Well, making somebody smoke weed at work sounds completely fucking ridiculous to me," said Brother James.

"Look James, I know sometimes we don't see eye-to-eye…but that's because I'm taller than you," said Ed Lover.

"Go and get us a hot chocoloate Ed," I said, as Brother James jumped from his bed, strutted menacingly to Ed Lover and, grabbing his wrist, pretended to give him a dead arm.

Ed Lover ignored my request for hot chocolate and returned to the book he was reading, *The Thought Gang* by Tibor Fishcer.

"Ha-ha, listen to this boys," he said, jabbing the inside of his book. "It's a description of Macclesfield. He calls it 'a place that doesn't exist for the outside world. Just as for many people here the outside world has no existence.'"

"That's not true," said Brother James, defensively. "Loads of people know about Macc."

"James," started Ed Lover, "hardly anybody has ever heard of Macclesfield and of those few people that have they only know two things about it: that it's home to the racist and homophobic rock band *The Macc Lads* and that its nickname is Smacclesfield because everybody who lives there is so bored they're all hooked on heroin."

"Bollocks," shouted Brother James angrily.

"Come on James," I said, "you have to admit, it's hardly the most enlightened of places. I was round Granddad's last week and Aunty Kathy's friend Tracey was there, one of the very few black people in the town, and when Fat Uncle Paul came in he said to Tracey, 'Oh, I knew you were here; I saw your shield and spear in the hallway.'"

Ed Lover spat out the coffee he'd just swigged.

"Moph's black and everyone gets on with him," said Brother James.

"That's true," I said, "although some people might think less of him if they knew he'd recently put his dick in a customer's brandy."

"Who's Moph?" asked Ed Lover.

"Lover, you'd love him," I said to Ed Lover.

"He's a friend of mine who works as a waiter in a restaurant called the Steak and Kebab in a village just outside of Macc called Prestbury, which is said to have more millionaires than anywhere else in Britain."

"That's right," said Brother James proudly.

"It's a fucking terrible place," I continued. "Have you ever noticed that every time we have a general election, the North West is a sea of red with this little blue spot in the middle – that's Macclesfield. It's where the piggly-wiggly-dicked Tory old-guard come to die and Prestbury is riddled with them. Moph had a party of them in there a few weeks ago who laughed at him when he cut his hand on a brandy glass they'd smashed. Although it looked like he was keeping his cool, he went back to the bar, poured a replacement brandy, unzipped his pants, lifted out his knob and stuck it in the guy's brandy, giving it a good wash. He took the brandy to the table with a grin on his face but just as he was about to serve it his knob started burning really badly. He was in tears when he dropped it on their table and legged it to the kitchen where he stuck it under a cold tap."

"What, and the guy drank it?" said Brother James.

"Every single drop," I told him. "Let me tell you, it pays not to behave like an idiot in restaurants."

*

"Go on Jimmy, get us a coffee," said Ed Lover to Brother James.

"Fuck off," snorted Brother James, groggy because he'd just woken up.

"Do you think you can flush paper down the toilets here James?" asked Ed Lover

"What the fuck are you talking about?" responded Brother James.

"Have you never been to a country where the sewage system can't handle paper?"

"Fuck off."

"I thought – no seriously – I thought Tenerife might be like that."

"It's not backwards there Ed."

"Oh, I dunno."

We visited a bar called Mangos after breakfast to buy cigars, where a pissed, stoned, pregnant and totally loopy Latina cut Ed Lover's cigar then turned to Brother James and started, "Hey lady, how do you want…" She realised her mistake as me and Ed Lover dropped from her view behind the counter as we fell to the floor giggling.

I went back to the hotel, and Ed Lover and Brother James went to Flamingo Park to buy some weed, which later sent me and Ed Lover into a talking frenzy and Brother James, who won't touch the stuff, to sleep.

Brother James got the fear at Flamingo Park when a local thug popped out of the bushes to announce his services. Ed Lover – who has bought weed all over Latin America – said Brother James's broken Spanish helped ease the situation, even though Brother James is only fluent in Spanish when he's having a conversation about building-materials, as he often did in Tenerife where he was working at the time as a joiner.

For our tea, we went to Little Havana, Miami's Cuban district. I was anticipating a tiny and colourful square with Cubans kicking back under the day's dying sun; instead we found enormous commercial roads with very little in the way of character.

Brother James was so hungry he strolled into the arms of a Dominican Republic restaurant where the waitress gave me a bemused look when I stressed "*sin carne, sin carne*", as I ordered my food. She responded to the idea of vegetarianism by getting the cook to fry chunks of cheese and put them on a bed of rice and black bean sauce, which was pretty tasty.

Brother James – who knows what he likes and likes what he knows – ordered steak and chips, which, when it arrived, was described by him as being "shit", which was enough to put the waitress into an apologetic spin and Ed Lover on one about respecting the fact that other cultures liked their meat cooked differently. "I knew I should have just had that chicken fadge-eater earlier," he moaned, ignoring Ed Lover.

The tables by ours picked up on the infectious argument and then started ones of their own, causing the fat, bald entertainer behind his Bontempi Hit organ to shout-sing in American-English and punch his keys to compete with the volume of the arguing tables.

We left Little Havana for a downtown bar where me and Brother James drank Miller Lite and looked for some Latin spirit among the white rock, reversed caps and the smiles and handshakes of strangers – "I love your accent." – "I love your accent." – "I love your accent." – "Do you really; that's absolutely fucking fascinating."

Ed Lover made a move on a girl from Greece. "I am from Greece," she told him, "and I have to tell you I don't find you attractive because we are a truthful people." We left shortly afterwards.

As we were leaving, Brother James decided to nip to the toilet, leaving me and Ed Lover to watch in wonder as the bouncer we were making idle conversation with suddenly leapt across the crowded room and fiercely grabbed Brother James's shoulders just as he opened the door to the gents because he thought Brother James was a girl – those blond locks, like busted aerials, consistently attracting unwanted signals.

"Get off me you fucking idiot," shouted Brother James.

The bouncer grabbed Brother James's arm and pulled him towards us.

"Leave him alone," I shouted, going over to help Brother James. Suddenly, another bouncer was pushing me and Ed Lover through the door. When

Brother James was dragged out he fell to the floor. One of the bouncers tried to help him up but Brother James kicked him on the shin. The bouncer punched Brother James in the eye.

*

"I reckon in Mexico we'll be shitting like fuckers," said Ed Lover.

"I thought I was going to get food poisoning last night," yawned Brother James, who had a sizeable black eye.

"Give it time," laughed Ed Lover.

"Right Ed," said Brother James, attempting a New York accent, "when I ask you to get me a cwoffee, you say to me, 'What did your last slave die of?'…and I'll say, 'answering back'."

I was remembering how it ended last night, outside the hotel with a taxi driver telling Brother James not to sleep with the prostitutes who pick up business in the lobby, and Brother James insisting on talking to them to discover how much they charged. Then we slumped into our room, fell onto our beds and started the journey to sleep, the only way left to us to ensure that our drunken bodies weren't sick. I drifted off with a bright yellow City of Miami parking-meter hood on my chest, which Ed Lover had stolen because he was leathered on vodka. As he slept, the city forgave him for his out-of-character petty theft because every night he snored a different musical, and the city, like all living things, needed variety.

*

We arrived in Mexico, which turned out to be, as they say in Macclesfield, a peak unique.

At Benito Juarez airport the three of us drank strong coffee and waited for the arrival of Timmy B, another brother and an exceptionally dirty rat. It's said that in any industry there are really only six people worth knowing and everybody else just follows the trends they set. In the British music industry, Timmy B is one of those six. He is also a fine guitar player, a hopeless gambler and an aspiring writer. He has two ideas for stories that I think are exceptional and may steal from him should it look like he's not intending to write them.

In Mexico, Timmy B would become a good

friend to Brother James, introducing him to, among other things, the whorehouses of Acapulco.

*

We were staying at the Hotel Gillow on Isabel la Catolica in the Centro Historica, close to the Zocalo, Mexico City's central square and the second-largest in the world after Moscow's Red Square. There were grand metal statues of the knight errant Don Quixote and his squire Sancho Panca in the lobby to greet us.

Also with us was Timmy B's mate, Ed with the Enormous Right Eye, whose right eye had ballooned to the size of a tennis ball because of stress. Ed with the Enormous Right Eye was a well-spoken bar owner and events promoter from Leeds.

All tired from travelling, the five of us strolled as far as the Zocalo and then collapsed in a café where the waiter wouldn't take my no for an answer – no I wasn't hungry, no I wasn't thirsty, honestly, no. He decided to make me a fruit juice from a pink fruit and gave it to me for free, which was very kind of him because it was beautiful and refreshing, exactly what I needed. Settled, we talked about how peaked out we were by how cheap everything was and how we caused the locals to pull intrigued faces.

*

Our first taste of fresh air came when we reached the top of the second-largest pyramid in the world; from up there I could see a green Volkswagen-shaped smog-cloud sitting on Mexico City and, if I dropped my eyes, a partially recovered walkway built by ancient kings.

We had befriended Marcos son of Marcos, a policeman for tourists, who found us chilling in the Zocalo at ten in the morning, waiting by the flagpole to see if Ursula Paradise would appear. Marcos son of Marcos advised us to take a trip to see the pyramids at Teotihuacan and let his father, Marcos Senior, take us there.

En route, Marcos Senior took a swerve before the Piramides del Sol y de La Luna into a giftshop next to a restaurant called Piramide Charlies – 'The oldest restaurant in the world. We serve the food that made the Aztecs strong.' In the giftshop a seasoned Mexican woman plied us with a fermented cactus juice drink that was 5% alcohol and 100% aphrodisiac.

"Drink these tequilas," she then said, so, of course, we did. At the time I had thought that all the tat she sold me was brilliant and sexy. Now I think it's laughably bad and, when I recently told Ed Lover as much, he reminded me how Brother James had bollocked him for not buying anything when he said he might. Brother James said it was rude considering the old woman gave us a lecture on the history of the cactus.

"But that's what they want you to think, you twat," Ed Lover had offered.

I still don't know what to do with the stuff I bought: a tablet of the god Packal, their dios de la felicidad (god of happiness), and a calendorio Azteca made from a stone called obsidiana, which is blue and has silver hands on it; and I have no idea if Brother James has kept his poncho or not.

At Piramide Charlies we made plans to separate. Ed with the Enormous Right Eye was keen to get to Oaxaca, so he went, just like that; Timmy B and Brother James wanted to leave for Acapulco; and Ed Lover, all he could think about was the possibility of making purple fountains with Ursula Paradise.

*

That morning my insides were wretched and tight, which can happen to me when I think about everything instead of one thing.

"Are you having normal?" asked Brother James.

"Am I having normal what?" I said

"Poos."

"Am I having normal poos? Yes, James, I am, to use your expression, having 'normal poos'."

"So am I, so why is everybody else complaining?"

"What the fuck are you talking about?"

Ed Lover bounded into the room.

"Ed's eye was a bit of a concern, wannit?"

"Aye, it was fucking enormous," replied Brother James.

"I was dreaming like a motherfucker last night; it's because I'm not smoking weed," said Ed Lover.

Brother James started telling a tale about his own dream and every third word was "fucking", and I wanted to tell him to improve his language, because words like that used loosely lose their edge. But I couldn't because I knew he'd snap at the suggestion. My dreams were crazy, very abstract, full of loud and violent voices, strange faces, the hotel, and kung-fu moves. It was all a bit odd and I felt like I must work hard to resolve these feelings inside me because I didn't like them nor did I want to inflict them on my amigos, especially Brother James, who I love so much it can make my heart hurt.

*

That night we ate in a Zona Rosa restaurant, the same one where Ed Lover had met Ursula Paradise over an ice-cream refill station, a couple of years earlier. Zona Rosa is a popular entertainment district for tourists. Touts there try to drag you into titty bars. As you leave Zona Rosa in their cars, the taxi drivers give you a run-down on the price of whores then try to take you back there, usually turning their cars around so that you have to tell them again and again that no, all you really want to do is just go back to your hotel.

Earlier, Ed Lover visited our room and his

parting gesture was a fart. "Thanks for that," I cried.

"Beg your P," he yelled from the corridor, "and don't worry, it won't smell."

Ed Lover has this theory that if his farts make a noise then they never have the energy to smell.

*

I had grown a beard and a sizeable cold sore and found that only deep-breathing the memory of colourful conversations with Brother James could unwind me.

Me, Ed Lover, Brother James and Timmy B were now at ease with this lively city, which sold stale doughnuts to western doughnuts like us, and amazing revolutionary t-shirts to raise money for the Zapatistas – the Mexican guerrillas who fight for the rights of their country's indigenous Indians. We walked from our hotel in the historical district towards Zona Rosa where I bought lots of the t-shirts – big white ones with images of guerrillas from the revolutionary party, the EZLN, preparing to fight – one with their hero Zapata standing rigid, another with Che Guevara looking as beautiful as ever. I also found a wonderful photograph of a Mexican guerrilla holding his wife and baby in his right arm, a gun in his left.

The next day we went to the Estadio Azteca to watch a local football team, Americas, play another Mexican side, Halchacoa. The Estadio Azteca is the 120,000-capacity football stadium where Diego 'Hand of God' Maradona halted England's ambitions to make it to the 1986 World Cup final and, in this stadium, our four western faces stuck out like a blind cobbler's thumb.

"For three Macc lads and a shandy-drinker from Cambridge, this is an amazing thing to be doing," I said as we took our seats and were offered beer and pizza to buy, which struck us as being very civilized, although Ed Lover did complain about there being no lemonade for his beer.

We were sat in front of a group of local mentalists who took to screaming passionately at the referee's decision when it went against Americas and whipping the back of our heads with their flags when Americas did well. They were amused by Timmy B's passionate enthusiasm for their team. He was wearing a club hat, blowing a horn and joining in the savaging of the referee. They made crazy gestures behind our backs when the beer-seller took a photograph of the four of us.

"Make sure it's only one-third sky," yelled Ed Lover at the beer-seller, espousing his one theory about what makes a good photograph.

"But Ed, there'll be no sky in this picture, you dick," piped-up Brother James.

"Shut it Jimmy," snapped Ed Lover, laughing.

Twenty minutes before full-time, Timmy B wisely suggested we leave the stadium to avoid the rush and any unwanted attention; we strolled to the exit, past the enquiring eyes of the stall-holders outside and into the arms of yet another demented taxi driver.

Earlier that day, from an elevated position, Timmy B had said that it must be the hand of God ensuring that the maniac taxi drivers in their green Beetles didn't twist metal proportionate to their driving skills. The concept of giving way is completely foreign to them and every journey we took eventually became a game of chicken with the oncoming traffic.

Within minutes of picking us up, the Estadio Azteca driver was darting between lanes at close to 80 miles-per-hour, and the more we protested the more he skinned his teeth and laughed a contagious laugh. "He's fucking loving it," yelled Ed Lover over the engine's rattle as we approached the peak of a tiny hill and the car took off, then landed with a swerve.

"Fucking hell! Enough mate, that's definitely enough," screamed Timmy B, putting his hand on the driver's shoulder, who, like every commission-hungry driver, began promoting the merits of prostitution as we approached the city centre. He made us even more nervous when he sped past the turning to our hotel because we'd heard stories about taxi drivers taking tourists, at gunpoint if necessary, to destinations other then the one requested and robbing them blind. It was OK though, he just took us to a titty bar, where we giggled like girls as he tried to tempt us inside with his toothless grin and enthusiastic air-massaging of an imaginary stripper's breasts.

*

The following morning, Brother James and Timmy B left for Acapulco, and Ed Lover went to look for Ursula Paradise again.

When we had arrived at the Hotel Gillow, Ed Lover had immediately located a telephone directory and together we tried to match the telephone number he had for Ursula with entries under Paradise. Remarkably, we managed to find a match for the phone number, and Ed Lover gave what he dearly hoped was Ursula Paradise's address to a taxi driver, and a letter that said, *I'll be by the flagpole at the Zocalo at ten in the morning on every morning I am here.*

That morning, she was there too. Beautiful.

*

Hello, I'm a little pissed. A few glasses of cheap wine are inside my empty stomach, which is inside a restaurant called La Opera Bar, which is inside Mexico's old town.

I wonder, do you ever wander and wonder while you're at it? I do. Today, close to the Zocalo, I found an ancient church where I rested and reflected with zero expectations. I remembered the last church in which I did this, a quaint Anglican one in a village just outside Cambridge. This one was more ornate. It was Catholic and it was sat on the foundations of an even older church, one from the pre-Hispanic era. As I stood underneath a crucified Christ, his face in pain, his limbs stretched, those nails in his hands, I realised that I really had nothing to worry about, so I came here to get pissed.

I'm eating alone because Ed Lover turned up in our room a little after six with Ursula Paradise, and I left them alone, figuring they'd probably want to get jiggy-with-it without me in the room.

*

"Would you like a song, boys?" said the Mexican guitarist enthusiastically, his guitar strapped to his fat belly. It was just after ten in the evening and me and Ed Lover were sat in the smoking room at the Hotel Gillow, a tight, cloudy lounge where the free peanuts were spiced to set your throat on fire.

"No Grassy-arse," said Ed Lover to Fat Belly.

"I charge only ten pesos per song," said Fat Belly, smiling.

"Oh, go on then," said Ed Lover.

Fat Belly played *Guantanamera*, a Cuban song about a beautiful woman, and we joined in enthusiastically at the chorus. I felt good and clean-shaven. During the day, a traditional barber had asked me if I wanted to save a moustache from my week-old beard. Laughing nervously, I gesticulated 'everything must go'. The seat dropped, he lathered me up and out came a blade with a Sweeney Todd sharpness that caused me to doubt acting on impulse.

After serenading us, Fat Belly sang "thank you boys," and winked at us, causing that dark room to get even darker and the smoke smokier and, as all eyes turned to me and Ed Lover, we retaliated by asking Fat Belly for some Beatles, which set them off, those burly men with their big old moustaches, into a medley of half-remembered melodies.

Earlier, Ed Lover had lingered outside the juice bar Yugos Canada with Ursula Paradise on his arm because he thought the staff there thought we were gay – they had got into the habit of giving us two forks to share our fruit yoghurt.

"Hey Ed, if I were a fruit what fruit would I be?" I asked him.

"Hey?"

"A gooseberry mate"

"A gooseberry, what's a fucking gooseberry? It's 'gusberry', you cunt."

Ed Lover is from the south of England. His gooseberry sounds like 'gusberry'. I am from the north of England. I pronounce it properly.

I spent a little time with Ed Lover and his lover that afternoon then got myself back to the hotel room where I thought I'd probably fall asleep because I didn't have much sleep in the night. I'd been waking up relieved that my nightmares weren't real and walking to the window where I hoped to see the gangs of men responsible for the maniac shouts and screams. In the middle of the night they sounded like demons and I wondered if that's really what they were, lost souls.

This seemed less likely the more I stayed awake. Slowly, I realised they were just men out late and enjoying themselves, but when you first wake that's not how it feels, not when you're drunk. When you wake up and you're drunk, it takes a while for you to leave your dreams behind you, and your nightmares.

*

That day I sat on Trotsky's toilet, added a pair of rusty pliers to the famous Russian's desk, preserved since his untimely death by pickaxe in 1940, and I floated serenely on a psychedelic boat in Xochimilco with Ed Lover, who would be on Mexican TV at the weekend advertising a fruit drink, and Ursula Paradise, who had a dance that was as simple and as powerful as a true sentence. Looking at the effect her dance was having on Ed Lover, I realised it was the hypnotic start of the way to love, a very feminine and enchanting seduction.

Me and Ed Lover also distracted a couple of hundred schoolgirls from practising their part in the celebration of the 1910 revolution. We had started at Yugos Canada with a shake, then strolled to the Zocalo, expecting to find Ursula Paradise standing by the flagpost; instead, we found two thousand Mexican schoolgirls.

A country with a bloody and turbulent past, Mexico snorted snot in the eyes of the Spanish conquistadors in 1910 under the leadership of

Francisco Madero of Coahuila, a previously imprisoned liberal who kicked off an almighty battle by asking his countrymen to revolt. The sight of me and Ed Lover wandering through their square in a daze peaked out these teenagers, who treated us to wave-giggles and kiss-blowing. Very cute.

When Ursula Paradise arrived she took us via the undergound to Xochimilco, where you can punt across a network of canals. Aqua-commerce at Xochimilco was as keen as its landlubbing relation. Massive punts carried a whole Mariachi band – something you'd never see on Cambridge's River Cam. There were boats that cooked us food and tried to sell us all sorts of unnecessary tat while we stared vacantly at their all-the-colours-of-the-rainbow canopies whose yellow was brighter than the sun that cooked them. All the while a grinning punter and his sweating dog guided our slow progress.

After Xochimilco, Coyoacan, the bohemian district where Leon Trotsky lived until his secretary's lover put that pickaxe in the back of his head. You can look around Trotsky's house, which also has a back garden full of hippy artists making nonsense and looking pleased with it. Keen to liberate a momento I nicked the pliers from an outhouse, then – feeling a bit guilty – decided to put them back. Though not where I found them but on the desk at which Trotsky was murdered, an addition I childishly hoped would confuse subsequent visitors until the curator removed them. I also hopped over a glass barrier and sat on Trotsky's toilet, a crime that Ed Lover has photographic evidence of. I busted him and Ursula snogging. "What would Trotsky think of that?" I yelled from the library, where I had a view of them tonsil-wrestling in the kitchen.

At Coyoacan, Ed Lover was press-ganged by a TV crew making a commercial for Del Monte orange juice. All he had to do, they told him, was sit on a park bench and make 'mmm...this is lovely' faces. It was to be shown on Channel 13 the following Sunday at 8.30pm. This would be the third time Ed Lover had made it onto television. The first time was in the Vietnamese village of My Lai. "Sadly," Ed Lover had told us, "My Lai is famous for a massacre the American army committed there. It's incredibly hard to get to. When I arrived, I was holding onto the back of a local who'd taken me there on his motorbike. There was a film crew making a documentary about the massacre and they filmed my arrival."

His second taste of fame came at the 1999 British pea-shooting championships in Ely, the smallest city in Britain. The year Ed Lover took part was a very controversial one because a young pea-shooter from Norwich took the trophy using a laser-guided shooter. Ed Lover and his friend Little John turned up stoned and decided it would be a good laugh to pea-shoot anybody who looked like a good target, including people being filmed by reputable broadcasters like Sky News. "Is there anybody here who isn't stoned?" demanded the cameraman. He filmed Ed Lover and Little John being battered by peas shot from the 12-inch steel pea-shooters belonging to a gaggle of fifty-year-old real ale drinkers from Wolverhampton.

Ed Lover was later dismayed that he had supported Del Monte, who are infamous for exploiting workers from the third world. Ed Lover is an informed consumer. For example, he detests Bacardi because of its support for America's embargo against Cuba, a device to make the poor ache harder than they already do.

*

On Saturday 20th November at 11am the furious clapping from the revolutionary celebrations woke me up. This was the sound of national pride, of applause and cheers for three columns of marching soldiers dressed in the colours of their national flag, who had started the procession at the Zocalo.

At first I thought the clapping was in the weird dream I was having, in which my Uncle Peter, who managed to balloon to maybe double his real-life twenty stone, gave me a Yorkshire Terrier to keep before it died in five days' time. He had the dog's kidney and the dog had his.

The crowd, which I watched from our balcony, then started booing for the first time – "boooo, boooo" they booed. On either side of the road, flanked by armed policemen and soldiers, were ten-thick lines of locals who were cheering their country's sporting heroes, unless it was a football team that they didn't like, in which case they booed.

"Are they cheering because I'm taking my trousers off?" questioned Ed Lover, who had beer-shits and was complaining about it.

"Liam, it's getting more surreal; they are clapping parachutists," he exclaimed, now hanging over our balcony. "That's absolutely insane."

Brother James had rung the night before to let us know that his flight from Acapulco had taken off then landed almost immediately because of a faulty engine. Brother James, Timmy B and Ed with the Enormous Right Eye were flying with an airline that had just had a plane blow up, mid-air, a few weeks previously. Brother James wasn't arsed; he'd visited a whorehouse, done a bungee jump and enjoyed some water sports.

"It's still going on Liam; Jesus Christ, we're onto hockey!"

Timmy B, a nervous traveller at the best of times, was, when I spoke to Brother James, in the airport lounge sitting in the puddle of colour that had drained from him, nervously biting his nails down to the bone.

"It's wrestlers Liam. Fucking hell Liam, human pyramids."

*

Brother James was back, Ed Lover had left for Ursula's house in the hills, Timmy B was on a flight home, Ed Who No Longer has an Enormous Right Eye was flying to New York, and I couldn't sleep because of the hideous din that was galloping unbridled from the decaying piece of German antiquity playing outside our hotel room.

If you can imagine an out-of-time and out-of-tune version of the *Chariots of Fire* theme tune, then you are some way to imagining the sound keeping me from sleep. Below my window, on the sidewalk of Isabel la Catolica, an old man dressed in beige and sweat-stained fatigues had a 1930s musical box strapped to his back. When he turned its handle it made the most appalling of rackets because it was old and knackered, and nor was it ever in time because his left hand, the free one, was always on the hunt for a donation from passers-by, which caused his right one to move irregularly.

*

"Do you want me to tell you what you should do

84

if somebody asks you outside for a fight?" said Brother James to Ed Lover, who was now sharing a room in the Hotel Gillow with Ursula Paradise following a weekend of crushing butterflies at her family's holiday home.

"Go on then," said Ed Lover enthusiastically.

"Right, well, if they say something like, 'Do you want to settle this outside?' you say, 'All right, I'll just finish my drink and if I'm not out there in ten minutes, you start without me'."

We were celebrating Ed Lover's return with 15-year-old Cuban rum, and I was back on the bed again, resting before our last night out. The conversation turned to cocaine, which we had all taken in the past except Brother James.

"What does it do to you Liam?" asked Brother James.

"Somebody once described cocaine to me as aftershave for the personality," I said.

"Huh," he grunted, "I can't see I'd ever need that. I'm very happy with my personality. In fact, if I believed in reincarnation, I'd want to come back as myself. When did you first take it?"

"It was in Macclesfield when I was living with

Toothpick," I said. "Do you remember that house?"

"I remember all those rectangular white patches your pictures left when you took them down because you'd stained the wallpaper with tobacco smoke," he said.

"Now, that was Teen Wolf."

"Who was Teen Wolf?" asked Ed Lover.

"It wasn't a who, it was a what," I replied. "A two-metre long piece of plastic tubing that we made into a bong. I had to kill it in the end – the thing was taking over. Me and Toothpick got that house when most people were still living at their mum and dads', so every night about a dozen lads would pile into our tiny lounge to watch *Prisoner Cell Block H*, play a video game called *Worms*, and smoke from Teen Wolf. And every time we got Teen Wolf out some dozy stoned bastard, usually me, would knock it over, sending dirty, brown, tobacco-filled bong water flooding across the carpet and spraying the settee or the armchair. One day I gave it a wash in bleach, which made it disgusting to smoke from so we had to chuck it."

"Urrrrh, and that was the house that Bull left his Spunk Mountain in, wasn't it?" remembered

Brother James.

"Fucking hell, yes it was," I said, wrinkling my face with the memory of Bull's Spunk Mountain.

"All right, what the fuck is Bull's Spunk Mountain?" asked Ed Lover.

"Well I never saw it myself," I replied. "In fact, I wasn't even living there when it happened. When I moved out, Toothpick had my room and a mate of his, Bull, took his old room, and, you know, they were just a pair of really sweaty boys. Every night Bull would crack-one-off onto his sheets and never bother to change them, building, over time, his Spunk Mountain. One night when Bull was away, another mate of Toothpick's stayed in Bull's bed, and just as Toothpick was getting his head down he heard a loud groan from his friend who'd rolled right onto the Spunk Mountain and cracked it…imagine that."

"Man, he could have just had posh ones and done it in a sock," said Brother James.

"It was a mad house. I'd become friends with a drug dealer called The Beard. The Beard had dozens of families growing weed for him in houses on council estates across Macclesfield, and during one of his business trips he popped in to have a reefer with me and Toothpick. As he was skinning-up, he said, 'Fancy a quick line?' and I just said, 'Yeah, why not?'

"I watched him carry on skinning-up on the arm of our armchair, which had a sprinkling of tiny holes from people letting rocks of hashish fall out of their joints and singe it. That armchair had been given to us by Toothpick's grandma, and I regularly witnessed him screaming 'what's wrong with the fucking ashtray?'

"When The Beard got up I followed him, giving Toothpick a shrug of my shoulders and a daft grin on the way out, and in our front room, on a cheap modern desk, The Beard tapped out some cocaine from a tightly-folded paper packet the size of two postage stamps while swinging on a knackered office chair. He put a banknote over the small and irregular blocks of powder and ran a credit card over the note again and again while looking at me like a crazed comedian about to pull a rabbit from a hat. The cocaine was then smooth and after a frenzy of taps and scrapes from the credit card it was split into two long lines. He rolled up the banknote to make a straw, stuck one end up his nose and put the other right over the line of cocaine and snorted it up. I was struck by quite how disgusting an idea that was but when he passed the note to me I did just the same."

"And then what happened?" asked Brother James.

"Nothing. 'Nothing's happening' was what I thought at first. And then my teeth went. The teeth at the front of your mouth, the top ones, lose all sensation around them and go numb like they're not teeth anymore but little tombstones that could fall out. And then I was back in the lounge, sitting upright on the settee feeling love and confidence at the same time as if they were the same thing, and then when that feeling wore off after about 20 minutes I was back in the front room doing it again. A few months later I was buying a couple of grammes a week off that cunt and I was seriously depressed because of it. I think cocaine is rotten stuff and should be avoided…unless you're at a party and somebody offers you a line, obviously.

"I really liked it when I first started doing it but increasingly I never felt like myself afterwards," I continued. "It got to the point where I could never be bigger than the drug – it always got the best of me. Then I went to a wedding with Crazy Legs in a lovely hotel just outside of Exeter. He'd brought a wrap of coke with him and when we left the reception to nip back to our hotel room to take some we walked right over the groom's brother, who was passed out on the grass because he'd had too much to drink.

"'We'll go straight back after we've done it and see how he is then,' we told each other. When we got back to the lawn we found the groom's elderly parents stood over their son trying to pick him up from the floor. I felt wretched that I'd stepped over my mate's brother like that and not taken him to bed before his mum and dad found him."

With nothing more to say, I read the previous day's food diary:

Wednesday

- *11.00a.m: Fruit yoghurt, chicken wrap, ham omelette and large coffee. 6 cigs.*
- *1p.m: Cheese sandwich, large bag of crisps, 3 chocolate bars and 1 milkshake. 4 cigs.*
- *3.00p.m: 6 beers and a packet of peanuts. 10 cigs.*
- *7.00p.m onwards: 6 beers and 4 rum and cokes. 10 cigs.*

*

For our last night together we were in Zona Rosa again and I was due to get my first taste of a whorehouse. Brother James had seen the inside of several of them in Acapulco, and when Ed Lover found the one we were looking for he sauntered inside like he owned the place. I have not since felt such apprehension at entering a public building. I didn't know what was going to happen and expected the worst, which, strangely, I thought meant getting my knob felt, not something I'd ordinarily complain about. Though I do like to have some say in it, like when and where it happens and who does it.

In Acapulco, Brother James and Timmy B were teased into almighty hard-ons as they sat drinking with whores who were happy to just toss them off there and then in front of the other patrons. The very idea of this was so at odds with the terribly conservative Englishness that was overcoming me, that I felt bound by an uptight straitjacket, one that didn't appear to be binding either Brother James or Ed Lover, who were giggling and giving each other dead arms as we took our seats.

"Don't like the look of yours much Eddy."

"James, you've got more rattle than a cow's got cunt, do you know that?"

"It's hot in here, innit? I'm sweating like a paedophile in a school yard."

I felt uncomfortable. They sat us right next to the slightly raised centrepiece of the room, a stage on which uninterested strippers strolled up and down like moody teenagers pacing in a shoe shop to test their new school shoes for comfort.

I had to look so I decided to focus on their eyes.

"Show us your greasy rat," an uncouth mouth from behind me shouted. "Don't be nasty, show us your pasty."

His friends roared.

The stripper responded by falling onto her back and spreading her legs in front of them.

I turned in my seat to face them. Looking back at me were a pair of fat, bald, scowling twins wearing England football-tops. They were holding their beer bottles like weapons, staring at me with a look that said, 'We're going to rip your fucking head off'.

Fuck that.

"Hey mate," I shouted at the fattest one, "just

because they're whores, there's no need for -"

Suddenly, a stripper's high-heeled shoe was on the back of my chair, the heel giving her support as she leaned into me, taking my glare from the dickhead twins to straight between her legs. A mini-cheer went up on our side of the stage. My heart started beating like a fucked clock, sweat exploded from my forehead and, recognising the terror in my face, her fanny started to talk to me.

"What is your problem?" it asked.

"Hey?"

"Why can't you just relax?"

I was dumbstruck.

"Huh," it snorted, and with that the stripper's leg swung across the back of my chair, leaving her to finish her turn.

I turned to find Ed Lover and Brother James looking at me with calm and enquiring eyes.

"You all right?" Ed Lover asked.

"Yeah, I'm fine mate, just a bit peaked-out. I could do with a drink. James, do you want a drink?"

"Yeah mate," he said, smiling. "I'd love one."

"Lovely," I said, turning to look for the man who had sat us there and finding him right behind me with three young girls by his side.

"Buy the lovely ladies a drink Señor."

It wasn't a question.

I looked up at them and smiled, and they smiled back, and I turned to Ed Lover and Brother James, who were also smiling, and back to the man, again a smiler. And with all those teeth showing I felt compelled to say, "OK, yes please, have a seat," despite feeling nervous enough to vomit.

The girls sat by us, mine so close to me our legs touched. She was beautiful like the beams of sunlight that pierce clouds and are sometimes called 'God's fingers', but the crashing waves of nervousness still broke furiously over me, pounding even harder when she took my hand and said, "Tell me your name?"

Six ludicrously overpriced drinks arrived. Ed Lover tapped me on the shoulder. He looked distressed.

"What's up?" I asked.

"They've got a thirst on mate," he said softly. "Look at that, they've nearly finished the first round; there's no way we're paying for a second – it's a fucking rip-off. Let's get out of here now before they sting us for another."

Brother James was nodding in agreement so we said hurried goodbyes, left money on the table and bolted for the exit.

On the way out, just near the exit, was a sunken pit with a stripper in it. She was holding a can of squirty cream and smiling at us. Brother James winked at her.

"Hey," she shouted up at him, "wanna lick cream from my pussy?"

"I dunno," he replied, grinning at her. "Is it full fat or semi-skimmed…I'm on a diet."

I pushed him through the exit, past the bouncers and onto the street.

"That was amazing," he said, "let's find another."

"Jesus Christ, no way," I replied. "I couldn't do it. I was getting so fucking nervous in there…my arse must look like the Japanese flag."

"Like a chewed tangerine," offered Ed Lover.

"Ah, you're talking about the rusty sheriff's badge," offered Brother James.

"Exactly…which right now looks like Grandma's favourite tea-towel holder, so can we please go home, please?"

"I can't believe you Liam," replied Brother

James. "It's our last night out in Mexico City, we are surrounded by bars full of naked women and you want to go back to the hotel. You are fucked up!"

*

From the whorehouse we went to a nightclub by the Hotel Gillow. Our plane left for London at five in the morning, so we decided we'd stay in the club until chucking-out time, get our bags from the hotel and then take a taxi to the airport.

The queue for the club was full of university students, and a gang of pretty girls at the end of it giggled enthusiastically as Ed Lover started talking to them in his charming blend of Mexican and English.

Inside, an uncharacteristically generous Ed Lover offered to buy all the girls a drink, and we started to get very drunk with them. Around two o'clock I was standing by the dancefloor propping myself up on Brother James and laughing because fizzing tequila was dribbling down my chin. The girls were bringing us glasses of tequila that they covered with their hands, slammed on tables and emptied into our open mouths. Wiping my chin with the back of my hand, I looked across the room and saw a wild-looking student pointing at Ed Lover, who was on the dancefloor passionately kissing one of the girls. Pointing Student was short and thin, wearing thick-rimmed glasses and had long, brittle hair that shot from his head in many directions as if it were charged with electricity and trying to escape. Pointing Student was talking excitedly to his friend, who was built like a brick shithouse. They crossed the dancefloor like sharks that had come up from deep down in the water because they'd picked up a scent.

I put my arm around Brother James and sharply swung him to face Ed Lover. Pointing Student and Brick Shithouse were standing next to Ed. Pointing Student cuffed the back of Ed Lover's head. Students on that part of the dancefloor had by then stopped dancing or were moving away. With Brother James beside me I ran onto the dancefloor, put my arms around Ed Lover's chest as he broke from kissing the girl, pulled him away and shouted, "You OK?"

Ed Lover calmly looked at Pointing Student, then turned to me and said, "Ah, fuck him! Here, meet his ex-girlfiend."

"Fucking hell Ed," I said, as he turned away from me, beckoning Pointing Student's Ex over for an introduction.

I ignored Ed Lover and put myself between him and Pointing Student, who looked at me with tiny angry eyes and called me a "filthy tourist pig".

With that Brother James launched himself past me, grabbed Pointing Student's shirt collars with his strong tradesman's grip, puffed his eyes out and spat the words "so psycho, so psycho" at him. Pointing Student was so shocked at having a demented looking Englishman announce himself as a psychopath that his glasses fell off. He then headbutted Brother James. Brother James went down like a sack of potatoes, and Pointing Student's Ex screamed, pushing Pointing Student away as she yelled at him. I dropped to Brother James's side. He was flat-out, his eyes were closed and blood was streaming from his nose. A circle formed around us. With a goalscorer's determination, Ed Lover ran at Pointing Student and kicked him hard in the balls. A sympathetic groan lifted from the crowd. Pointing Student's Ex then leapt onto Ed Lover's back. Ed Lover toppled to the floor as the girl sunk her fingernails into his scalp. Her friends attacked Ed Lover too. A fat one sat on him and windmilled lumbering thumps on his back as he lay face down, spreadeagled and wriggling.

Suddenly, Brother James came to. He leapt to his feet and charged Pointing Student, knocking him to the floor then pummelling his head with quick and vicious thumps. Brick Shithouse then launched at Brother James. As Brick Shithouse tried to wrestle Brother James from Pointing Student I punched Brick Shithouse right on the ear. Brick Shithouse winced with the pain then stood up and squared his huge frame against mine. He tried to kick me in the balls, but I managed to pull a move from my tiny kung-fu arsenal, putting my knees together to catch his ankle before his foot reached its target. This surprised him so I punched him in the eye and swung my elbow into his temple, a move that I'd practised many times in kung-fu lessons and couldn't believe I'd pulled it off.

With confidence I went for him again. He smacked me in the mouth so hard that I went flying backwards, straight into Ed Lover and the girls. As I fell on them, Brick Shithouse jumped on top of me and started to strangle me. Brother James, who now had his fingers up Pointing Student's nose and was using them to playfully guide Pointing Student's head left then right, got up to help me just as a small army of bouncers snatched the three of us from the dancefloor.

The bouncers marched us to the top of the stairs and threw us down them. They then scooped us up at the bottom and carried us into the alley next to the club, where they dumped us and walked away. Through fuzzy eyes I could make out Brother James getting to his feet and jumping on the back of one of the bouncers. "James, no!" I yelled. It was too late. The bouncer threw Brother James to the floor and grabbed his hands. Another bouncer grabbed his feet. Despite his wild thrashing, the bouncers swung him back and forth and, as me and Ed Lover stumbled to his defence, they launched him into a skip.

We ran to the skip, clutching its sides as we nervously peered inside. Brother James was kneeling on bags of waste food and screaming challenges at the bouncers. He tried to get to his feet but the bags split, sinking his legs into a nasty ooze of rotten food. We hauled him out, and the three of us staggered to the hotel, not saying very much. The hotel staff wouldn't let us inside to collect our bags. The porter brought them to us instead, then waved us away like stray dogs. We stopped a taxi and in the back seat, leaning on Brother James, I drifted into a prophetic sleep.

*

An angel visited me while I slept.

"Hiya," I said.

"Hello."

"How are you?"

"I'm fine thank you, and yourself?"

"Good, yeah, good."

"You don't know who I am do you?"

"No idea, no."

"I'm one of the angels of God, the Archangel Petra Selvacleary of Wigan."

"They have angels from Wigan?"

"Absolutely. I am the angel that looks after New Year's resolutions."

"They need an angel for that?"

"For part of the year, yes."

"What, just January?"

"Well, that's certainly when I'm at my busiest, but I'm also pretty busy with it 'til the spring, then it really tails off."

"What about now in November?"

"Oh, I get this month off usually."

"Oh…are you now on your holidays then?"

"No. I've been asked by God to come and give you a message."

"Oh, Jesus."

"Incidentally, have you given any thought to what your forthcoming New Year's resolutions will be?"

"It's a bit early, isn't it?"

"Have you or not?"

"Well, as it happens, there are three that I'm thinking about."

"Go on."

"To take better care of my teeth, to wear better socks, and to never to sit down on the toilet just to wee, which, I hate to admit, I've found myself doing a few times this year."

"They sound like good ones. So, do you know the story of Abraham in the book of *Genesis*?"

"Sorry, I don't."

"Well, God said to Abraham, 'Kill me a son'.

Abe says, 'Man, you must be puttin' me on'. God says, 'No.' Abe says, 'What?' God says, 'You can do what you want Abe, but the next time you see me comin' you better run'."

The angel started laughing then sung, "Well Abe says, 'Where do you want this killin' done?' God says, 'Out on Highway 61'." And then the angel bowed his magnificent head and, pretending he had a guitar strapped around his shoulder, started playing the air, his hands cupping and strumming the imaginary guitar excitedly, his head nodding so that his long, thick black locks swung around us.

"What, that's written in the bible?" I asked.

"No, you fucking idiot," he said, looking up from his air-guitar. "Jesus wept, you're a case…they are lyrics from a Bob Dylan song. Look, this is the message – never look for birds of this year in the nests of the last."

'It is no easy matter to give novelty to old subjects, authority to new, to impart lustre to rusty things, lights to the obscure and mysterious, to throw a charm over what is distasteful, to command credence for doubtful matters, to give nature to everything, and to arrange everything according to its nature.'

Pliny the Elder

JESUS LIVES IN VENEZUELA

We were lounging in the living room of our Islington flat, which we had recently furnished with a substantial aubergine couch from Habitat and a print of the Great Wave of Kanagawa, when we heard Brother James arrive. The calm summer air carried his thick Macclesfield accent through the open window as he thanked the taxi driver. "Cheers pal," he bellowed, "keep the change."

I leapt from the comfort of the aubergine couch like one of those boats being tossed by the Great Wave, sticking my head out of the living-room window to yell, "Brother James, over here."

He spun round as fast as he could with an enormous rucksack on his back and shout-burped "Liam" at me, which provoked a mild tut from My Claire.

Grinning, he crossed the road, strutted up the

wide Edwardian stone steps to our flat, and when he was level with me, and only a few feet away, showed off his new skinhead haircut by furiously rubbing his head with both hands. He was wearing a t-shirt emblazoned with the logo of his new company. He puffed out his chest, losing his balance because of the heavy rucksack.

"Oh shit," he laughed, dramatically grabbing the iron railings between us to steady himself.

He put his finger on the doorbell and left it there, leaving the dreadful buzz to hang until I picked up the intercom.

"What the fuck do you want?" I yelled.

"Let me in motherfucker," he yelled back with a New York accent.

"Fuck you man," I replied, copying his style.

"No, fuck you man."

Click.

I opened the door to our flat and bundled him from the hallway into our living room, slipped my right leg behind his left leg and pushed at his shoulders, guiding him down to the floor, sticking him there like an upturned turtle. I sat on his stomach, grabbed his cheeks and brought his forehead to my mouth and gently kissed it.

"Hello brother," I said, jumping up, holding out a hand and pulling him upright.

"Hey," he said, "you be careful; you know I broke my leg in two places."

"Yes James," I replied, dryly, "in Spain and in France."

"Hello James," said My Claire tentatively, leaning to kiss him.

"All right Claire?" Brother James replied, responding with a hurried peck on her cheek. He dropped his rucksack to the floor and excitedly told us that the logo on his t-shirt (a peach with a smiley face) was also sprayed on his new van.

"Guess what it says on there as well, on the van?" he said hurriedly.

"What?" I asked, grinning too.

"'You are behind Peachyface Joinery, just like our competitors'," he said. "Good that, innit?"

"That's brilliant," I replied.

"Would you like a cup of tea, James?" My Claire asked.

"Yes please love, two sugars ta, not too milky."

Over tea and crumpets, Brother James amused us with a New York story. One day, while walking across the streets looking for tat to buy, Brother James came across a sleeping Alsatian in a builders' yard. He shout-burped "bollocks" at the dog and it immediately woke from its slumber and launched itself at him, barking and snarling ferociously, gnawing at the railings between them. Later that day, Brother James, Ed Lover and Smashed-up Face were, by Brother James's design, walking down the same street. Just as the three of them reached the yard, Brother James put out his right arm and started running, his hand banging against each of the railings. On cue, the crazed Alsatian ran at the fence just as an innocent Ed Lover drew level with it.

"Lover shit himself," laughed Brother James infectiously.

*

We were due to fly to Caracas early the following morning. That night, as My Claire made Brother James's bed for him, she talked to him about her work in the television industry.

"Do you know the television presenter Kate Thornton?" she asked.

"Does her dad have a chocolate shop?" he replied.

*

Even though it was a new city to me, Caracas was comfortable like the company of an old friend, and it was also very, very hot. We were staying in a Sabana Grande hotel, Hotel Tampa, Room 803, a matrimonial suite. Baking under the room's stone porch, me, My Claire and Brother James unenthusiastically chewed on rank coconut flesh while Ed Lover was downstairs in Room 108 making purple fountains with Ursula Paradise, who had arrived from Mexico City that afternoon.

*

"Come on Liam, you've got to admit it, the women here are the loveliest in the world," said Ed Lover, who was sharing a cigarette with me on the porch as Brother James, My Claire and Ursula Paradise chatted.

"Ursula, you have a lovely figure, what is your secret?" asked My Claire, refusing to take

Ed's bait.

"My secret?" she responded. "I dance; yes, I dance a lot."

"Do you want to know my secret, girls?" asked Brother James.

The girls paused. Brother James was a bit of a fat bastard at the time and they weren't sure how to take his comment.

"Does it involve pies James?" said Ed Lover, raising his tone to make the question sound reproachful.

I smiled at Brother James and turned to gaze at the cause of all the noise, at the dense confusion of blaring cars, trucks, buses and bikes beneath us. The vehicles were all knackered like the miserable-looking buildings around them, whose rooftops were patrolled by starving Rottweilers.

"You know what?" said Brother James to My Claire, throwing a big piece of coconut over the balcony. "I've had four poos today, and not little ones, really big ones, full of fibre…that's great, innit?"

"Yes, fantastic," interrupted Ed Lover, saving My Claire from having to respond. "So, what time are we flying to Gran Roque tomorrow?"

*

"There is shit to do, but that doesn't matter –
you're in paradise," said Leo, owner of Posada
Aqua Marina. He was a dreadful boaster though a
very handsome and charming man. We were on
the island of Gran Roque, the largest habitable
island of the Los Roques archipelago. "My Posada
is without a doubt the most beautiful on Gran
Roque," continued Leo. "I provide everything:
three meals a day, boat trips to the beaches on the
other islands, parasols, scuba gear…everything."

"Great," we said in unison, "have you got any
rooms?"

"Nope, fully booked now until mid-May. You
can stay for a beer though if you'd like."

At $98 per person per night it was beyond our
budget anyway, but we did stay for a beer because
he was playing The Stone Roses on his stereo.
After a pleasant wander down more dusty streets
we settled for the nearby Posada Rosana and Ed
Lover named its owner Ho Chin Minh because of
a clump of hair growing from a mole on her chin.

"Who the fuck is Ho Chin Minh?" said Brother

James, causing Ed Lover to offer up a detailed account of Ho Chi Minh's life as we walked to the supermarket for pre-dinner snacks.

After dinner, I rested on my bed, a single, scrawny and tattered mattress on a concrete base, and I wrote. Occasionally, I would look up to watch My Claire putting her make-up on, thinking she looked incredibly cute.

"Are you nearly ready to go?" she asked.

"I'm ready, baby," I replied softly.

All my family love My Claire, even the members of it that don't like me. It's incredible. I asked her, some months before, to go easy with my heart, to keep it safe, which she does with such care. I can hardly believe what I feel. Safe. Safely in love.

We had arrived on Gran Roque in a six-seater propeller plane, and, probably because the pilot was very overweight and sweating so violently, all of us in our minds devised ways to survive should he pass out.

*

"Don't go in there, that's our home," said a voice from under the parasol next to ours.

"Ah, sorry, we're from England."

"Oh, OK, take what you want."

"Nice one."

Brother James was telling us all how he would have liked our encounter with the family of locals on the nearby island of Madaka to turn out. We had taken the ten-minute boat ride to Madaka from Gran Roque and, upon landing, mistook a local house for a shop and their parasol for our own. They did let us stay under their parasol but wouldn't let us borrow their dinghy. There was nothing to do on Madaka, so we just relaxed. The sand was white. The sea was green. The pelicans were enormous. They rose, they fell and they dived, and My Claire smiled, and me and Brother James swam, and Ed Lover cuddled Ursula Paradise. It was perfect.

*

Ed Lover entertained us on the beach at Madaka with stories from the English public schools that he'd boarded at as a teenager. He was expelled from one of them after being accused of leading the group of pupils that had broken into the school's new gymnasium and trashed it two weeks before it was due to be opened by a local dignitary. Ed Lover wasn't actually in the gym when this happened. He had previously broken into it though to study its construction because construction fascinates him, and he had also climbed the clock tower and changed the time on the unwound clock to two minutes to midnight in honour of the song *Two Minutes to Midnight* by the British heavy metal band Iron Maiden. None of the teachers noticed this subtle clue. What they did notice however was their new gym having its insides ripped out a few evenings later and when they pinned this 'atrocity' on Ed Lover, who had been in bed at the time, he would say in his defence that you can take a horse to water but you can't make it drink.

That evening, reckoned the headmaster, Ed Lover had told some of the other kids in his dormitory not only how to get into the gym, which was still under construction, but also which bits would crumble most spectacularly if pushed, that he knew they were all impressionable enough to do it, and that while they were on the subject of Ed Lover's behaviour he should also know that the school, despite having no proof, also suspected him of being involved in the recent bricking-up of the entrance to the school chapel.

"You didn't do that, did you?" I asked.

"Of course I fucking did it," he said, suddenly animated. "For fuck's sake, the fucking cunts!"

As Ursula Paradise soothed him with a gentle reprimand and a light back massage, he began another story, about the Jamaican twins who had helped Ed Lover brick up the chapel door and who became famous for having afros that betrayed their recent behaviour.

The brothers loved to grow their afros big, and they, like Ed Lover, were ingenious pranksters who drove teachers to their wits' end. They spent their two-week suspension for desecrating the school chapel at home in Jamaica, where their deeply Anglican mother decided to punish them by shaving their heads and sending them back to a school with a letter inviting the teaching staff to do the same whenever her boys misbehaved.

When the other kids found out about this, they would wait until one of them had a big afro and then start a fight with him in the playground or canteen, causing one of the many racist teachers to cheerfully grab a brother and take him to the staff room for a shearing.

*

"I was thinking how long it would take Liam to die, so that we could use his bloated body as a raft," offered Ed Lover, discussing what he would have done had we been forced to bail out of the six-seater plane.

"I would have fucking landed it," said Brother James.

"I have actually flown a Chipmunk before," said My Claire, who was attached to the RAF as a teenager.

"Isn't that a small animal?" asked Ed Lover.

"It would have been down to luck, surely," I said.

"We were over water, so we would have had a chance," said My Claire.

"Think what would have happened to Claire's shoes," said Ed Lover. "The reports would have said an unknown amount of people have drowned but judging from the amount of shoes recovered it must have been a party of at least 25."

*

"Aren't you bored, Liam?" asked Brother James.

"With what, mate?" I replied.

"With Claire," he said flatly.

"What do you mean?"

"Well, how long have you been seeing her now?"

"Nearly a year."

"And have you fucked anyone else while you've been seeing her?"

"No, of course not."

"Really?"

"Does that surprise you?" I asked him.

"Well, I couldn't do it. I've never had a bird for longer than a few months without fucking another one."

"But she's good for me James. I thought you'd like her, that you'd be happy for me."

"What, happy because you're stuck in a relationship?"

"I don't feel stuck. I feel liberated. It wouldn't do you any harm, you know."

"Liberated," he laughed, viciously. "You've always got a big word, haven't you?"

"I try," I said, becoming defensive. "And you could always try learning a few more."

"Oh, fuck you, university boy. Here, I've got one for you." He shout-burped "twat" in my face.

*

Posada Rosana charged $35 per person per night, with no extra charge for the cockroaches in the bathroom, which shot out of a showerhead that was actually the end of a hosepipe. Nor for filling buckets full of water from a well outside of the Posada and then pouring that water into the cistern so that you could flush the toilet. Nor for Brother James coming to the breakfast table in just his black pants, saying, "I've got a bit of an abscess, I think," drawing our attention to the enormous bulge in his pants, from which he then pulled out an apple, thrusting it at me.

"Fancy a bite?"

"Fuck off."

Oh, and how loudly My Claire screamed when, while showering, she discovered a dirty big cockroach snuggled inside the folds of her exfoliating puff. It was the sound of absolute terror and it drew me from the yard to our bedroom in a flash. I found her pinned against the cold and uneven tiles, naked, no longer screaming but trembling, and pointing at the offending puff. Cautiously, I approached it, lifted it by its string and gently shook it until a merry cockroach fell out, lazily raising its head to the running water for a while before following the water's journey down the drain.

*

The children of Gran Roque play marbles with an accuracy that would wow any British child. Crouched metres from their opponents' marbles, they can deftly rest theirs between thumb and forefinger, and then…whoosh…the target is hit with a consistency that we'd struggle to achieve were we playing the same game with basketballs. In Gran Roque, the locals and holiday-makers share the same earthy streets and everyone smiles as if there is no need to distinguish neighbour from visitor because, after all, why bother about sharing the serenity when there is so much to go around?

*

Fish for dinner, fish for breakfast – everywhere fish and fishermen.

We were all lazing under a canopy on another island, Francisca, enjoying more of the same. There was a hut nearby selling…fish. Earlier we had gathered around the island's one phone to ring our mums and wish them Happy Mother's Day.

"Hiya Mum."

"Oh, hiya darling, how are you?"

"Great, just great, we're having a really good time. We're on a little Caribbean island called Francisca, and I'm stood here with James and Claire, and Ed and Ursula are here too. It's really beautiful and really hot. We're ringing to say Happy Mother's Day."

"But it's not till next week Liam," said my mum.

"Ah."

My Claire had rung her mum before I made my call. My Claire's mum had said, "Oh, thank you dear," and must have been wondering why My Claire's brother Jimmy had failed to ring.

Ed Lover had been refusing all day to ring his mum and insisted later, with an enormous grin on his face, that it wasn't because he knew it wasn't Mother's Day, which nobody believed.

There was lots of laughter under the parasol as Ed Lover retold the story of his visit the evening before to the tiny airport at Gran Roque. He had gone there with Ursula to ask if it was possible for them to leave a day early. When the soldier radioed the mainland to check, he also confirmed that, yes, 'Gay Liam Kerby' was still leaving on the 21st. My first name is Gary. I never use it because my dad's name is also Gary, and my mum, even though she named me, didn't want the confusion of having two Garys in the house.

For some reason the airline's administrators had dropped the 'r' from the name.

"Gay Liam Kerby," repeated Ed Lover loudly, a boyish chant that had Brother James in stitches again, and even My Claire, who had also heard the story at least three times, was grinning broadly at the hilarity that Ed Lover and Brother James were finding in this simple mistake.

*

Leo was pissed that night, a really pissed pissed that confirmed our suspicions that his by-day shaking was caused by his vociferous at-night drinking. "Do you smoke?" he asked us, staggering out of the bar we were entering. "Do you guys snort?" He chopped imaginary lines of cocaine for us, each one larger than the last and informed us how fucked he intended to get us. Then he waltzed past us and into an argument with another islander in a sandy alleyway between two small stone buildings. Him and his adversary then kicked sand at each other using legs so lacking in balance that each kick threatened to do more damage to the kicker than its target.

*

Ho Chin Minh served up scrambled eggs for breakfast.

"Oh joy," exclaimed Ed Lover, "finally, some eggs."

My Claire grinned at me when the smell from

the table reached her nose and then she stared sympathetically at Ed Lover, her eyes widening with apprehension, her lips tightening as she sucked them between her teeth, as Ed Lover took his first eager mouthful.

"Fucking fucking hell!" he yelled, spitting out his food, "scrambled fucking fish."

Defeated by the ubiquity of the fish of this archipelago, Ed Lover slowly rose from the table and, looking miserable, returned to his room to help Ursula Paradise pack their rucksacks before that morning's flight back to the mainland.

After seeing off Ed Lover and Ursula Paradise, the three of us strolled into the island's scuba-diving shop to book an instructor for the afternoon. We got Fernando, a short, muscular Venezuelan with a confident charm and over thirty years of experience in diving the local waters, he told us.

"Liam, you are in South America; we are shorter here," said Fernando, rummaging among his wet-suits for one that might fit me, as My Claire and Brother James slipped comfortably into theirs. From his shop we took the short boat-journey across a choppy sea to Francisco, the sharp wind cutting across our faces as we concentrated on stopping the air tanks slipping away from between our legs. On the shore at Francisco we strapped the tanks to our backs and waddled into the clear, warm water, slowly submerging ourselves as Fernando instructed us on how to breathe the air from the tanks. After only half-an-hour of instruction, we were packed back onto the boat and taken out to sea, to the spot from which we'd launch our dive.

My Claire had never dived before. Me and Brother James had only done it the once ourselves, in Tenerife with a friend of our dad's who took us down to about twenty metres, again with only a meagre amount of tuition on the shore beforehand. I sat at the edge of Fernando's boat with my back to the choppy sea thinking, 'Am I really prepared for this?' one hand on my goggles, the other on my breathing apparatus, and then toppled backwards, followed by Brother James and My Claire. Immediately it was uncomfortable, with Fernando trying to shout instructions as the waves battered us. We had only submerged a few metres when My Claire began to panic and signalled to Fernando that she needed to go up, but Fernando didn't take her seriously, and instead motioned for her to be calm and not to worry. I could see tears rolling from My Claire's eyes and I became worried that unless Fernando took her back up to the boat she would start hyperventilating and have a panic attack.

I had to do something so I poked him in the side and protested too, leaving our tiny instructor with no choice but to signal for us all to return to the surface, where me and Brother James bobbed about as Fernando's assistant helped My Claire back onto the boat, its bow narrowly missing our heads as it reared then slapped back down.

Fernando then took me and Brother James down several metres to a coral bed, which was serene compared to the attitude we had been treated to at the surface, a tranquillity that even the tiny eel that popped its tiny head out of its tiny cave and stretched its tiny mouth to screech at us could not break – nor Fernando either when he started poking lobsters, sending them scuttling magnificently away.

Back at the surface, My Claire was gently laughing with Fernando's mate, and I was so relieved to find her in such a good mood that I suggested the three of us visit Francisco's only restaurant and order some fresh lobster, a delicious meal that was to crown my newfound carnivorous state.

I had been a vegetarian for ten years until the previous summer when I had visited my mum and dad and Brother James in Tenerife, got pissed with Brother James and stumbled into the arms of a kebab shop, its neon sign hailing me like a Holy Grail. Five minutes later I was sat outside with the other pissheads wholeheartedly scoffing a chicken kebab. For a while after that I would only eat meat when I was drunk, tackling my denial in sweaty and rotten kebab shops in North London. Following My Claire's guidance – "Liam, you are eating absolute shit; if you're going to eat meat you might as well eat good meat." – I started eating organic chicken and fish, and really enjoyed it. I struggled with eating red meat for a couple of years after that first chicken kebab but eventually turned to the dark side completely – and now I'll eat anything.

As a vegetarian I had always argued that any meat-eater should be happy to see their food killed before they eat it, even kill it themselves if needs be, because, simply, that's how it gets to your plate. That afternoon, we watched open-mouthed as the chef at Francisco's restaurant waded out to his sea pot, pulled a lobster from it, weighed it, placed it on a stone slab and then thrust a knife into its head, which caused it to flap terribly. He then cut it in half, walked the pieces into the kitchen, and threw them onto the grill, leaving us to debate how it was that the lobster could still act like it was alive, jumping about on the grill, when it was in fact in two pieces.

At no point did I shudder, while Brother James and My Claire, both committed meat-eaters, were clearly uneasy with this spectacle. My Granddad, who had previously questioned my sexuality because I didn't eat meat, would have been proud, though I tended to take what he said with a pinch of salt. And I was proud on our second dive when My Claire, who had cried a few tears at lunch because of what she believed to be her inadequacy, took the plunge and joined us under the shallow waters of a calm Francisco bay.

The journey back to Gran Roque from Francisco was hilarious. Fernando was arseholed on Polar beer, singing at the top of his voice and steering his boat by standing above the handle that controlled the rudder, and guiding it with his right foot instead of his hand, teasing the accelerator with his toes then gripping it suddenly, causing the front of the boat to lift dramatically, us to laugh, and Fernando's mate to try and stop our tanks from rolling everywhere; luckily, all of us were safe in the knowledge that Fernando was unlikely to topple his livelihood.

*

My Claire was drying her hair and wondering why there seemed to be so little power in her hairdryer, a puzzle solved when the cockroach she had been slowly roasting for the last couple of minutes spat out of the nozzle straight into the arms of our fan, which knocked the poor bugger for six into the bathroom, where it looked up, shook its head, got its bearings and then scuttled for cover behind the toilet. Seeing so many cockroaches widened my interest in them enough to find two observations about them interesting: on the Wyclef album *The Ecleftic*, Wyclef's sister suggests that the Jean family are like cockroaches, and towards the close of *One Hundred Years of Solitude* by Gabriel Garcia Marques, which I'd just read, Aureliano Buendio made friends in a bookshop by entering into a debate about cockroaches. In the book, he reveals...actually, I can't tell you, you'll have to read it yourself because I gave my copy to Ursula Paradise, who gave me her Spanish copy that she happened to have with her. Although Ursula didn't say too much to us, leaving us hanging on her every word when she did construct a reply, I knew she'd have my copy mastered before I even dared to open hers.

*

"I'd rather be pumped full of heroin and asked to do the Salsa," said Ed Lover.

I was travelling in a jeep with My Claire, Brother James and Ed Lover, heading from Caracas airport back to Hotel Tampa. We had just seen Ursula Paradise off, who was flying back to Mexico. The last time we did this journey from the airport into town we had seen the aftermath of three car crashes. Again we saw a crash. This time all those involved stood close to and pointed at the burning engine of a pick-up, paying no heed to the possibility of it blowing-up.

Ed's consternation came in response to the suggestion by an airport tour-operator called Jesus that we go to the Angel Falls by bus, an eight-hour trip ("Have you ever tried to sleep on a bus when the video is blasting out?" Ed Lover had asked), then take a short plane journey, arriving at base camp at 8.30am for a day that would take in a lot of trekking and sleeping at night in a hammock ("which can be fucking uncomfortable until you get used to it," he had continued).

Instead, we accepted Jesus' suggestion that we take a three-hour car journey with Him from Caracas into the Park Henri Pittier, where we were anticipating doing much of the same stuff that we had done on Gran Roque – which was four-fifths of fuck-all.

*

"I tell you what, if I were Prime Minister, I'd put an end to same-race marriages," said Ed Lover, putting the lid on an argument that had boiled up over breakfast then simmered as we strolled along Sabana Grande with Brother James declaring, "Liam, I don't give a fuck about what you say. All your examples are about what happens in London. I don't live in fucking London. I don't care about fucking London. I live in Macclesfield. I'm happy with the job I do and I don't give a fuck about anything you have to say."

I had made the fatal mistake of starting a political argument about race. My comments about gangs of Romanian pick-pockets in London started Brother James off on a theory that suggested all Romanians should therefore be banned from entering the country. I had parried this with the suggestion that we have a duty of care to the oppressed and suggested he get to grips with some of the facts before he launch into one of his half-cocked arguments.

*

"Liam, we have done very well; I'm very pleased," said Ed Lover, back on the porch of the matrimonial suite at Hotel Tampa.

"Yeah, but Brother James is so anti-drugs,"

I replied.

"Fuck it, man, he is, but he doesn't know everything about it and he isn't prepared to listen to any arguments."

*

The four of us had popped up at Belles Artes, looking out for potential pick-pockets, which according to the *Lonely Planet* were rife: "Pickpocket at 11 o'clock," offered Ed Lover, bouncing about like a child wired by fizzy drinks.

The market at Belles Artes was similar to the ones we had encountered in Mexico City. Every stall was selling something more obscure than its neighbour, so obscure that you wondered how its owner could possibly make a living from it. How could anyone survive, for example, from selling dirty brown wind-up plastic rats that whizz along the floor once you've wound them, their brown plastic tails rotating as they take their short journey? I bought ten of these plastic rats for people at work thinking that we would have rat races on the wooden floor in the office, which, of course, never happened. In fact the only one who got any use out of them was the wag who decided to wind up his rat and trap it under the dustbin on the night our cleaner was due to visit, correctly guessing that it would shoot out from underneath the bin when she lifted it and put the fear of God into her.

The four of us walked casually between these stalls, nodding to the hopeful store-holders or lightly chatting among ourselves. Me and Ed Lover saw the boys first. Brother James and My Claire saw them too, and stopped walking. At the edge of the market, teenage boys were sat on empty stalls, swinging their legs and piping a shrill whistle at passers-by, and muttering offers of drugs, of marijuana and cocaine. Ed Lover approached these young drug dealers and I looked back at My Claire and Brother James. My Claire looked concerned. Brother James looked angry.

Ed Lover started talking to the boys. They asked him to join them for a walk, but he said no. He told them he would buy marijuana from them if they brought it to him. Suddenly, one of them dropped off the stall and into the park, where he grabbed a plastic bag from the scrub. He pulled a handful of weed from the bag and placed it on the wall between us. Ed Lover gave another boy the money and told me to put the weed into my trouser pocket. There was so much weed that it spilled over as I clumsily tried to shove it all in. The boys were all grinning at me. "More money," one of them said. He was tall and thin, wearing a white vest, a baseball cap and gold chains around his neck. "More money now!" he said quickly, walking towards me. I looked at Ed Lover. "Let's go," he said. I turned quickly, and at the top of his voice the boy shouted "more money" again, then started laughing.

"Are you ok darling?" asked My Claire. She put her hand into mine and I gratefully clutched it.

"Yeah, yeah, good – you all right?" I replied.

"Yes, I was a little worried though. That man was watching everything."

A middle-aged man in a beige suit whose white shirt was undone at the collar was looking right at me.

Brother James had started walking ahead of us, purposefully walking as fast as he could, forcing us to choose between losing him and keeping up with him.

"How's Brother James?" I asked.

"Livid."

"Oh great."

I caught up with Brother James at the entrance to the train station, grabbing his shoulder. He turned to snap "Fuck off!" at me.

"James, James," I said, concerned and surprised at the viciousness of his response. "What's wrong?"

"You know what's wrong, Liam. You and Ed are fucking pathetic. I am very disappointed in you both, very disappointed. Can you not just go for a couple of weeks without smoking that shit?"

I let him join the queue for tickets as I looked out for My Claire and Ed Lover. When I looked back, Brother James was in the queue and talking to the man in the beige suit. Oh shit. My heart raced. When Ed Lover and My Claire sauntered into the station I looked at My Claire and nodded towards Beige Man. I could tell that she had seen what I had seen. Beige Man, standing with his hands on his hips, was wearing a holster with a gun in it.

As I bought my ticket, I had one eye on Brother James, who was speeding through the ticket barrier, and the other on Beige Man, who was staring at me, My Claire and Ed Lover. The three of us walked quickly through the barrier and past Brother James, who was now walking as slowly as he possibly could, dragging one foot after the other as if he were in pain. "James, not now mate," I shouted at him, "we're in trouble."

He could see that Ed Lover and My Claire had started running. "Just run," I shouted at him. He shot forward, passing me and joining Ed Lover and My Claire on the platform's edge.

"Where is he?" said My Claire, whose fair skin was reddening.

"I don't know," I replied. "Let's just get on this train."

When the train pulled in we all jumped on.

"What's going on?" said Brother James.

Nobody answered him.

"What is going on?" he repeated, kicking my ankle.

I ignored him, fixing my eyes on the platform.

"He's here," said Ed Lover.

Beige Man was running along the platform. He ran straight past our carriage. The doors bleeped, signalling they were about to close, when Beige Man suddenly turned on his heels and jumped between the closing doors, landing right in front of me, grinning. My Claire then quickly pushed Beige Man hard in the chest and he fell backwards onto the platform as the doors closed in front of him.

At the next station, we jumped off the train and bolted for the exit. Outside we walked quickly, darting across busy roads until we saw a taxi to take us back to the hotel.

Back in our hotel room, me and Ed Lover skinned up and, as the smoke travelled into my lungs then my brain, I relaxed and opened a beer and started gibbering about how good our trip through the mountains and into the village of Porto Columbia was going to be.

"Liam, a bit of commonsense please," barked Ed Lover as he was leaving our room. "Can you make sure you put the weed down into the inside of your bag when you pack it please?"

"Where are you putting yours?" I asked him.

"Just in a sock among all my dirty underwear in a plastic bag…do that if you want."

"OK, I will."

*

The next morning we got up early and I packed

in a rush, forgetting Ed Lover's warning, and after a final smoke put the weed in a plastic bag and packed it at the top of my rucksack.

Jesus was late. The four of us sat there trying to remember exactly what we'd said to Him at the airport: if we had said midday and if we had definitely said we were staying at Hotel Tampa. An hour passed. And then another.

"Fucking hell, He's not fucking coming is He," said Brother James, echoing all of our fears.

And just then we heard it, His van rumbling up the narrow corridor by the side of Hotel Tampa, His arm hanging loosely out of the driver's side-window, His dopey grin settled across His face, dark shades and long and slightly greasy hair giving Him the look of a likeable rogue.

"Sorry I'm late," He said to us as we shoved our bags into His van. "We will drive quickly through the hills, I promise."

The mountain drive got increasingly terrifying as Jesus kept his word and drove quickly. At first it was fun, with Him taking hairpin bends as fast as He could, and us being thrown into one half of the van, Him saying dispassionately, "Put your seatbelts on," and us wrestling with broken straps and rusted buckles as another turn approached.

But then it got scary. The canopy of the forest started to encroach upon the road and gradually the light left us, and we started passing small huddles of peasants who stared at us, looking sad and resentful as we hurried past them. The four of us became quiet. We were unsure of ourselves. And then it happened. We spun round a corner and directly in front of us, maybe 200 metres away, was an army checkpoint.

"Ah, the army," said Jesus.

Oh fuck. The hurried glances that ricocheted between us confirmed that we were all thinking the same thing: me and Ed Lover were carrying weed. What did that mean to a Venezuelan soldier? We had no idea and we really didn't want to find out.

My fear was distracted by Jesus calmly reaching into His glove compartment and pulling out a gun and stashing it in a hole in His dashboard where ordinarily a stereo would have been.

Our eyes met over His rear-view mirror.

"Do not worry," He said, chuckling. "Everyone in Venezuela has a gun but I don't have a licence for this one and if they find it we will be here all night. Better I hide it."

He looked away and I continued to stare at His mirror until the van slowed down, the door swung open and a soldier with a machine gun motioned us all out of the van. Jesus spoke calmly to the soldier in charge and we all tried to look relaxed and comfortable and did a terrible job of it. The soldiers matched our half-smiles with stony glares. Then a dog appeared with its handler and leapt inside our van for a sniff around. I looked at Ed Lover, remembering his advice and wishing so badly that I'd taken it.

"Would you like to buy them a coffee?"

I was waiting for its bark.

"Liam, would you like to buy the army a coffee?" repeated Jesus.

"Yes, oh God, yes, of course, whatever they want."

"You holiday?" said the soldier in charge.

Ed Lover responded in his broken Spanish, which seemed to please the soldier. His crooked smile was soon broken though by the sound of the dog's bark. Oh my fucking Jesus Christ, it's found the weed. With everybody else I looked towards the handler and his dog as they left our van. Jesus approached the handler with a coffee, and the handler smiled at us, motioning for us to get back inside. Apparently there was nothing of interest in there. Thank the Lord.

"They were looking for cocaine," said Jesus, starting His van for the short journey to Porto Columbia.

*

"They can fucking drink, those fucking Slavs," said Ed Lover at breakfast the following morning, hungover from drinking 50 per cent proof spirits with a couple of Slavic lads who were also staying at Posada Gonzo, a stone house much like the Posadas of Gran Roque, only this one was priced at $25 per room, which we thought was very reasonable . The night before we had eaten grand food for a couple of pounds and drunk bottles of Polar beer for 30 pence, mixing with European drum-beating post-grads with marijuana leaf tattoos, and holiday-makers from South America and Africa.

It was very tranquil swinging on the hammock after breakfast and writing about the previous day's adventure, gazing idly between sentences at the wonderful view of the Caribbean sea from our porch.

*

Before breakfast I had left the room that me and My Claire were sharing for Brother James's and Ed Lover's room to bum some toothpaste from them. I could hear them arguing from outside.

"No, I think you'll find that I came into the room as quietly as possible and that's why I'm pissed off with you, you cunt," shouted Ed Lover, who had obviously woken Brother James up following his drinking session with the Slavs.

"No Ed...then why did you wake me up, you fucking dick?"

"Look, you can't fucking beat me James. If you want to criticise everything that I am then fuck you; I am the way I am and I'm happy with it."

This was not a good time to be asking for toothpaste.

I banged on their door.

"What?" snapped Brother James.

"You got any toothpaste?"

*

That afternoon we had a kung-fu accident that left Ed Lover's feet decorated with plasters. We were practising simple blocks and punches on the roof of our building when Ed Lover decided it would be a good idea to try and kick me with both legs at the same time, rather than leave one on the ground for balance. Neither foot struck me, but one of them did make contact, on its way to the deck, with the stone pillar next to me. As he shouted "Fucking fuck!" at the pain, I resisted letting out the ruck of laughter building in my belly.

"Fucking hell, are you all right mate?" I asked, offering him my hand. He used me for support as he hobbled down from the roof.

On the porch we found Brother James swinging on the hammock and exposing his ideas on relationships with My Claire: "I haven't really got time for one at the moment, but if I did decide to get a bird she would have to be really fit, well-off, and let me do whatever I want to do…like shagging other birds," he offered.

"You don't have much respect for women, do you?" said My Claire.

"No, not really Claire," he replied, leaping off the hammock, smiling cynically at My Claire, shout-burping "Bollocks" into my face then announcing he was off for a walk.

"Hold on Jimmy, I'll come with you; I want to dip my feet in the sea," said Ed Lover. "Just let me get some plasters."

"You know what?" I asked My Claire, after swinging in the hammock for a little while, watching Ed Lover and Brother James taking the short walk to the sea and wondering how best to warm this cold moment.

"What?" she said, a little sharply.

"Well, if you think about it," I started, "what he's saying isn't that bad. I mean, you're really fit, you're well-off, and you let me do what I want to do…so, in many ways, we are the same."

"Oh no, you are very, very different, Liam," she replied. "You, for example, do not think, and I quote, that 'all women are prostitutes as you pay for it one way or the other.' I just can't be arsed with it, Liam. I just don't want to be arguing about these things while I'm on holiday, especially with a 23-year-old who doesn't know shit from butter."

She joined me on the hammock and we swung and read, and held each other until we heard Brother James and Ed Lover returning, finishing an argument as they reached the porch.

"Ed, I am here to educate you, not to undermine you," said Brother James, "and I wouldn't say that being generous is a fault."

"It is if you're so insecure you give everything away," replied Ed Lover.

Ed Lover plonked himself down on the chair next to us, picked up the Tetris and stuck his head in it, clearly in an awful mood. Brother James went back into his room for a lie down, slamming the door behind him.

Everyone was miserable. Marvellous.

*

I woke up that morning to find My Claire sobbing quietly in our bed.

"Oh my God, what's wrong?" I asked.

"I can't stand this, Liam," she said, punctuating

each word with a sharp intake of air as she tried to talk and cry at the same time. "Why is he doing this? Why is he spoiling my holiday? Why is he being so nasty to me? Why is he constantly ignoring me or putting me down?"

The really frustrating thing for My Claire was that she was capable of dishing out incredible tongue-lashings, but she held back out of respect for the fact that we were all on holiday, trying to enjoy precious time away from work. I kissed her, cuddled her, told her everything was going to be all right, grabbed two boogie boards, left our room, tapped lightly on Brother James's and Ed Lover's door, and Brother James groggy, me secretly seething, we headed to the beach.

"What's up with you?" he asked, looking at me tensely, sensing my anger.

"I am pissed off with you is what's up, and you are about to find out why."

"What do you mean?"

"What do I mean? Is it not blindingly fucking obvious to you right now why I would take great pleasure in smacking you in the mouth, you arrogant little shit? Is it not?"

"Liam. What are you going on about?"

"James, if you don't tell me now – tell me what it is that she has done to deserve this from you, why you are turning on her, and me and Ed – then we are going to seriously fall out, fall out like we used to do when we were teenagers, and I really don't want that, and I hope that you don't want that, because I love you, but you have to explain to me what the fuck is going on."

I was raving. We crossed a quaint wooden bridge, where heavy stones caught the peaceful trickle of the sea-bound stream, and my mood upset the peace and quiet.

He didn't say anything; he just walked.

I stayed quiet too.

We carried on walking along the steep, winding dirt track to the beach.

"Look Liam," he started, "I don't have to justify myself to any of you. Look at it from my point-of-view. Usually these holidays are about the lads having a laugh, then suddenly you and Ed bring your fucking girlfriends and I'm the fucking gooseberry, expected to get along with people that I don't even know."

"Well, yes you are, but that's not what you're doing; you have instead managed to make Claire's holiday miserable for her. I have just left her crying her eyes out, James, because you are being so fucking mean to her all the time, and it's not funny. It's not your usual sarcasm, it's just a meanness that I've never seen in you before, and I don't like it. I really, really like her James. What the fuck has she ever done to you?"

He started to reply but his voice let him down, he choked, and I looked hard at him, at his eyes, where tears were starting to spill, and I was startled, immediately regretting everything I had said as tears started to flood from his beautiful eyes. His lips were shaking, then his shoulders and suddenly his whole body, as a wail released itself from inside him. Quickly I held him to me, grabbed him tight. These tears betrayed a pain so deep, the shuddering of his body released a tension so strong, that it went on for minutes, me holding him and repeating softly, "James, James, hey, it's OK." And finally the words came from him, the most powerful and significant words that have ever been spoken to me.

"I don't want to lose you Liam. I just don't want to lose you."

"What do you mean James? You're not going to

lose me."

"I am," he said, his body still shaking, tears still pouring, having to catch a breath before he could continue. "I know I am. You're going to forget about me, and I'll never get a girlfriend and you and Claire won't want me around because I've been such a shit to her, and...I'm losing you."

I took a deep breath, aware that I needed every fibre in me to communicate my love for this man I thought I knew so well but who still had the capacity to surprise me.

"James," I said solemnly. "Brother James, look into my eyes, look at me; I am your brother, I will always be your brother and I will always love you the most. You are everything to me. There is nothing, nothing on this earth with the power to come between you and me, nothing..."

"Yeah, but -"

"James, there are no buts, please believe me when I say that. James, my love for you is so strong there is no force known to man or nature that could even threaten it, even make it tremble. We are strong. Incredibly fucking strong. Tight as tight can be. And what is this nonsense about you not being able to get a girlfriend. You are a beautiful, beautiful, funny man."

And so the conversation continued, us walking towards the beach, Brother James pouring out all these feelings that had been fizzing inside him, and finally, thank God, the cork had popped and the ill-tasting brew had released itself, and our amazing conversation continued. We made it to the beach with our boogie boards, surfed a little, got out when the waves got too big, and had a brief cuddle on the beach, showing our love and affection for each other.

"All right, Liam, that's enough; get off me you big puff."

"Come here, give us a kiss."

On our walk back we saw Jesus and told Him we would return shortly with My Claire and Ed Lover. I returned to my room to find My Claire packed and ready to go, and I hugged her and told her some of what had happened, and as we left our room together we met Brother James and Ed Lover on the balcony. I was hopeful that Brother James would say something to My Claire, to all of us, hug her too maybe – but that would have been too much too soon, not Brother James's style, and I think that My Claire knew and respected that.

However, the mood definitely lightened, and Brother James was immediately, noticeably and genuinely more polite to her, which, admittedly, wasn't difficult. Before we returned to Jesus' van I told Ed Lover what had happened and he said that he was glad, and that Brother James had been very sheepish on his return but seemed lively again now.

*

We were hoping that Jesus having His son and His mother with Him for the return journey would have a positive effect on His driving. No such luck. Ed Lover's utterance in the back of the van of "Oh fucking fuck," following, unbelievably, a lecture at breakfast about his inappropriate swearing in public, put Jesus in a spin, and He careered back down the mountain at breakneck speeds. He had started the journey telling us, "We will go slow on the return. To get here, we went fast; now we will go slow only." I prayed that He was the Son of God and that our journey back home would be blessed, and that we would not provoke the head-on collision that seemed imminent.

*

My letter to Brother James…

Dear James,

I trust this letter finds you well, and Mum and Dad too.

Since getting home I have had a pain under my heart continually from remembering that I made you cry on holiday and wondering if I have damaged our irreplaceable brotherly love. I'm hoping that you do not regret releasing your sorrows and torments, the sobs that rushed through your body like an angry sea, and that you remember I am not your judge, but your brother, and that you can always speak to me about what you feel without any misgivings or fear.

One day soon you will meet the woman you are

going to marry – I am confident about this because I know that you have all the virtues required to make you respected and happy – and when you do I will continue taking refuge in you when I am alarmed by everything, and I will always try to depict for you things just the way I see them.

Nothing important will change.
Your brother,
Liam.

*

Despite the guns and the tears, we still had a good time in Venezuela. There were classic lines, there was weed and alcohol, and, thankfully, eventually, tranquillity, and also a time when I told Brother James that it was my intention, that year, to ask My Claire to marry me.

So, Claire, will you marry me?

POSTSCRIPT

Me and My Claire are married now. Brother James and Ed Lover were the best men at our wedding.

Brother James and My Claire are good friends. In his speech, Brother James described My Claire as "genuine and lovely".

In my speech, I said this:

"Claire, your honesty, your humour, your passion, your intelligence, the comfort that I feel when I am with you, these things have become everything to me, and by standing here today and saying 'Yes' you will be my wife, you have answered what I think is the most difficult question that life can throw at all of us, which is: who will I grow old with? It's you. And now that I know the answer to that question, everything else in life seems relatively straightforward."

Ed Lover's speech wasn't so sentimental. This is

how it started:

"The thought of talking to you today has made me very nervous, so I decided to prepare a few lines…and now that I've had them, I do feel much more confident."

ACKNOWLEDGEMENTS

To learn writing from classics is like carving an axe handle with an axe – the model is right in your hand.
Ju Li

I have stolen great lines from good friends and hope to find their forgiveness over a pint.

I have also turned over two suicidal American authors, lifted lines from the film *Withnail and I,* and drawn from letters by the South American revolutionary Jose Marti.

The description of Mrs Buckle in New York in the Basis of Truth is indebted to Ernest Hemingway's description of F. Scott Fitzgerald in *A Moveable Feast*, his book about life in Paris in the 1920s.

From John Kennedy Toole's *A Confederacy of Dunces*, a rant by Ignatius J. Reilly is attributed to the New York scriptwriter Heinous Name Dropper.

Were these authors alive today, I wonder what they'd say about what I've done?

They would probably know about the other things that Ju Li wrote: that the first taboo in writing is to walk behind others because if you follow someone you will always be behind, and that the relationship of the writer to works of the past is complex, since what may inspire your work will also kill what you write if you fail to make it new.

Comfortingly, Hemingway once wrote that 'some writers are only born to help another writer to write one sentence', and guessing he wouldn't have excluded himself makes me feel much better about the whole thing.

Legend Press

Independent Book Publisher

This book has been published by vibrant publishing company Legend Press. If you enjoyed reading it then you can help make it a major hit. Just follow these three easy steps:

1. Recommend it
Pass it onto a friend to spread word-of-mouth or, if now you've got your hands on this copy you don't want to let it go, just tell your friend to buy their own or maybe get it for them as a gift. Copies are available with special deals and discounts from our own website and from all good bookshops and online outlets.

2. Review it
It's never been easier to write an online review of a book you love and can be done on Amazon, Waterstones.com, WHSmith.co.uk and many more. You could also talk about it or link to it on your own blog or social networking site.

3. Read another of our great titles
We've got a wide range of diverse modern fiction and it's all waiting to be read by fresh-thinking readers like you! Come to us direct at www.legendpress.co.uk to take advantage of our superb discounts. (Plus, if you email info@legendpress.co.uk just after placing your order and quote 'WORD OF MOUTH', we will send another book with your order absolutely free!)

Thank you for being part of our word of mouth campaign.

info@legendpress.co.uk
www.legendpress.co.uk